READY MEAL TECHNOLOGY

Edited by

Andrea Menlove, J. Sainsbury plc

Published by
Leatherhead Publishing
Randalls Road, Leatherhead, Surrey KT22 7RY, England

First Edition 2002
ISBN No: 1 904007 29 5

Printed and bound in the UK by IBT Global, 1B Barking Business Centre, 25 Thames Road, Barking, London IG11 OJP

FOREWORD

WHY? This book has been written to bridge the gap between the lack of technical knowledge in the literature and the growing need for practical guidance in a fast-growing sector of the food industry.

WHAT? The scope for the writers of this book was defined as "Ready meals as they are normally classified at point of sale. Such meals would be expected to contain components that have been cooked at least once, either separately or together as a meal. They are purchased chilled, frozen or even ambient and require heating for best results." So, for this book, our definition covers pre-cooked products such as curries, lasagne, Chinese, etc., which are classified by their origin, but salads and pizzas, etc., are outside the scope as they contain raw components.

WHO? The intended audience is graduates, people new to this technology, or existing manufacturers, as a refresher, as they look to branch out. It may also be useful for undergraduates, and school children may use it as an example of one sector of food technology.

HOW? The chapters, which represent distinct areas for consideration, are written by experts, and were designed so that they do not necessarily give all the answers, but make readers think about what they want rather than being told this is the way to do it. The approach taken in this book is to pose a series of questions to help you to decide which type of ready meal operation is the most appropriate. The book is not meant to be an exhaustive guide, but to give food for thought in regard to the aspects involved in designing a product, its package and its operation of manufacture.

Ready meals represent a complex topic, as the nature of these products tends to mean that a lot of raw materials are used, creating a complex multicomponent product. As a result, there are a number of ways in which the products can be compiled, which in turn often directly influences product quality. For example, the safest and easiest way to make a ready meal is to assemble all the components in their raw state, seal the container, then heat it all in one go. Problems with this route could be as follows:

i) Each component takes a different length of time to cook, so the cooking regime must be set to take account of the longest to cook – hence the potential of over-cooking in the rest of the components, and consequent taste issues.

ii) The packaging would need to be robust to allow the components to be cooked within, causing pack distortion and a pack that is not easy to open by the consumer.

iii) Separation issues might arise as the product would be difficult to agitate effectively.

iv) Products cannot be given any finish for improved visual appeal, e.g. grilled cheese topping.

While the above process is useful for certain products, higher quality is often achieved only by breaking the process down into parts and reassembling them. The complexity of this area is increased by a number of other factors/variables, which are discussed in this book, covering the whole or part of the process, such as marketing, packaging, process, product and environment.

The book is laid out in a logical step-wise sequence, outlining the fundamental principles, by chapter, that need to be controlled in order to develop a product or process. Each chapter title poses a series of questions, which raise further questions to develop the inquiring thought process needed; ready meal technology is very much about how basic food technology principles are applied to develop a practical solution.

The approach taken in this book is to discuss these issues, to enable you to abstract the relevant key questions to start your analysis, which will then produce your chosen product. We do not discuss the manufacture of products specifically. The information in this book will help you to devise the appropriate production plan for your process. So, for lasagne, you might distil the following important criteria:

- Raw material quality – what level of visual lean in mince, to ensure a tender moist product?
- Microbial – what sauce temperature (<5 °C, >60 °C) for your product?
- Determining quality – what cut for mince for price point required?
- Designing process – consider the order of process, how many layers of pasta/meat and sauce?

I would like to thank the writers of the chapters for their specialist knowledge, LFRA for its help in organising its production, my husband for his patience and J. Sainsbury for giving me the opportunity to produce this book.

I hope you enjoy this book, in this exciting area, which is worthy of further discussion. The future depends on so many factors, but will surely be driven by consumer demand as we change our lifestyle to purchasing meals that are ready to cook. This will then demand even more attention from the technical world.

Andrea Menlove (nee Brainwood)

CONTENTS

CONTRIBUTORS

Ms Danuta Tomoszek
Oscar Meyer Ltd
Furnham Road
Chard
Somerset
TA20 1AA

Ms Vicky Nolan
Product Innovations
Lovegroves Barn
Fieldside,
Long Wittenham
Abingdon
Oxon
OX14 4QB

Mr Tony McMullen
Saxon Valley
Montgomery Way
Stratton Business Park
Biggleswade
Bedfordshire
SG18 8QB

Mr Howard Griffiths
Geest plc
White House Chambers
West Marsh Road
Spalding
Lincolnshire
PE11 2AL

Dr Bizhan Pourkamailian
McDonalds Europe
Lyoner Strasse 34
D-60528 Frankfurt am Main
Germany

Mr David Jeffries
Oscar Meyer Ltd
Furnham Road
Chard
Somerset
TA20 1AA

Ms Margaret Stevenson
Cavaghan & Gray plc
Brunel House
Brunel Way
Carlisle
Cumbria
CA1 3NQ

Mrs Anne and Mr Henry Emblem
Emblem Packaging Solutions
8 Duloe Road
St Neots
Cambridgeshire
PE19 8FQ

Mr Alec Kyriakides and
Mr Steven Batchford
Sainsbury's Supermarkets Ltd
33 Holborn
London
EC1N 2HT

1. WHAT IS A READY MEAL?

Danuta Tomoszek

1.1 Introduction

What is a ready meal? This used to be a relatively simple question, but as cooking skills decline, and as retailers offer more and more part or fully prepared products, the boundary between ready meals and prepared meat and vegetables is blurring, and ready meals are becoming more and more difficult to define. For example, consumers can now buy traditional ready meals that are frozen, chilled or ambient; they can buy kits for putting together complete meals, including prepared vegetables and sauces; they can buy ready meals that are cooked or raw, and they can buy prepared meats such as chicken breasts filled with spinach and cheese. Consumers can also now buy these in different parts of the supermarket – the chilled ready meals section, the frozen and ambient sections, the deli, the raw meat sections and the fresh vegetable section.

Eventually, the concept of ready meals may be overtaken, replaced by an assumption that most food bought in the supermarket is pre-prepared in some way. The definition may in future change to reflect whether the food is bought to eat that evening, or is bought to be stored in the refrigerator or freezer.

It remains to be seen whether there will be a backlash against prepared foods, as there has been against the perceived "interference" with our foods, and the growth of the organic and GM free markets, or whether we will simply no longer have the time to use anything but pre-prepared meals.

1.2 Why Do Consumers Buy Ready Meals?

Consumers buy ready meals because they need the convenience they offer.

Figure 1.1 shows some of the factors that have changed the lives of this generation.

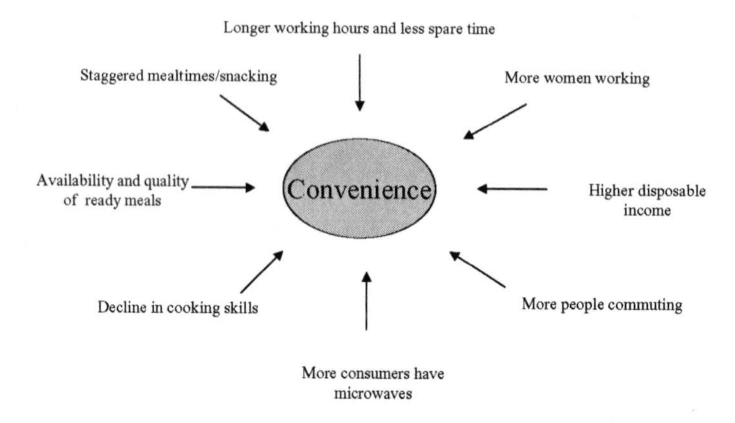

Fig. 1.1. Why do consumers need greater convenience?

Lifestyle changes that have influenced eating habits include:-

- Fifty-five per cent of women now work, so they don't have time to start preparing meals when they get home (source: Office for National Statistics – Labour Market Trends).
- The current generation is being brought up by parents who are more likely to be working, and who have to rely more on pre-prepared foods. This means that they are not growing up with a mother who cooks from scratch, so are not learning the skills.
- We are working longer hours, especially in Britain.
- We have higher disposable incomes, and so have the money to spend on pre-prepared foods.
- We no longer sit down as a family for a meal – families are tending more and more to eat separately, and using the fridge as a virtual takeaway. For example, young children may eat early in the evening, possibly when they get back from school, with the parents eating later on, and older children grabbing snacks before going out, or when they get in late.
- We also tend to eat more snacks. We used to sit down to a plate filled with meat and two or three vegetables. Now, our meals take a much more varied format – they don't necessarily have meat, we may eat two

small meals in place of one big one, or we may "graze" all day, eating small quantities at regular intervals.

- Around 70% of households now have a microwave oven - which allows us to eat within about 5 minutes of looking for something in the fridge. Also, around 80% of households have a freezer of some sort, which makes it easy to keep some meals in stock at all times.

All of these lifestyle changes mean that consumers have a growing need for convenient products.

1.3 How Do Consumers Define Convenience?

All prepared foods offer consumers convenience, but where do ready meals sit along the "convenience scale"? Figure 1.2 shows the spectrum from least convenient (home made) to most convenient (home delivery).

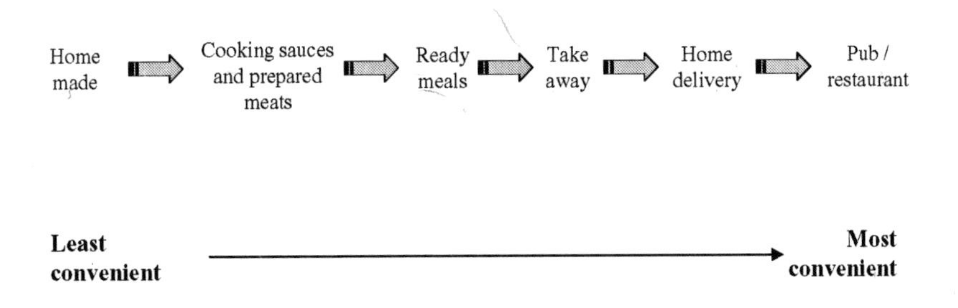

Fig. 1.2. The convenience scale

Factors considered in determining the relative convenience of a meal include the following:-

- Home made involves buying all the separate ingredients needed for a meal, and preparing it from scratch – a lot of time needs to be invested in this option by the consumer.

- Cooking sauces and prepared meats cut out some of the work, but still need more shopping and preparation than ready meals.

- Ready meals offer a complete meal or meal centre, to which consumers may add a side dish, usually vegetables or bread. They also remove some of the washing up, as meals can be heated in their trays, which are then thrown away. Some consumers will eat a ready meal from the tray, which can reduce washing up to one fork (very appealing to certain people!).

- Take away removes the need for any cooking at all, but the consumer still has to go out to buy it and then take it home, serve it up and clear up afterwards.
- Home delivery, after ordering by telephone, means that the consumer doesn't have to leave the comfort of their armchair – particularly appealing on a cold winter's evening!
- Pubs and restaurants also take out all the cooking, along with the need to take the meal home, put it on plates and wash up afterwards.

Interestingly, consumers appear to rate convenience on how much effort they have to put into the meal preparation process, rather than the time it takes. For example, most ready meals are still cooked in the oven, despite the widespread ownership of microwave ovens, which can cook a ready meal in around a quarter of the time.

So the factors that offer consumers convenience can be summarised as:

- Very little preparation required.
- Not much washing up.
- The right amount for that meal occasion.
- Doesn't need much to go with it – ideally nothing or just some vegetables or bread.
- Easy to buy and store.

Ready meals offer all of the above, so this is why they are generally regarded as being particularly convenient.

1.4 How Do Consumers Define a Ready Meal?

So what do consumers currently perceive a ready meal to be? Any of the following could be considered to be a ready meal:

Chicken Kiev	Main course soup	Stir-fry kit
Meat pie with pastry	Curry	Casserole
Fresh pasta and sauce	Quiche	Pizza
Snacks	Sandwiches	Vegetables and a sauce
Meat and roast potatoes	Filled Yorkshire puddings	Meat and a sauce

And they could be in any of the following formats:

- Chilled
- Frozen
- Ambient

Also, they may be:

- Pre-cooked
- Raw

We know that consumers don't distinguish between raw and cooked ready meals – after all, they look exactly the same if they are both packaged in a tray and a cardboard sleeve, and they are both treated the same way – put into the oven for 25 minutes.

This range covers a huge array of products, which all meet the consumer's need for a convenient meal. However, in order to define a category that is manageable and consistent, three factors can be applied:

- Quality
- Ease of preparation
- Meal status

1.4.1 Quality

Ready meals are generally considered to be of a better quality in terms of content and nutrition than items such as pastry pies, breaded meat such as kievs and pizza.

1.4.2 Ease of preparation

To be considered a ready meal, the meal must generally be fully prepared apart from final assembly and reheating. There is a fine line with prepared meats, usually sold within the butchery section, which may include sachets of sauce, or a topping or stuffing. These products are often in the same type of packaging as ready meals, with a plastic tray and a cardboard sleeve, and are considered by consumers to effectively be ready meals, but are merchandised with raw meat.

1.4.3 Meal status

Ready meals are usually accorded a certain status, and in fact, for a lot of occasional purchasers, are seen as a "treat". This means that the definition excludes a lot of convenient foods, such as sandwiches and soups, which are not usually eaten on the same sort of occasions as a ready meal – they are more likely to be eaten as snacks or lunch, whereas a ready meal is mostly eaten as an evening meal; around 60% of ready meals are eaten in the evening (source: TNS Family Food Panel Survey).

1.4.4 Summary

To summarise then, a ready meal can be defined as follows:

- It consists of either meat and/or vegetables, usually with some sort of sauce.
- When served, it forms the centre of a meal or is a complete meal in its own right.
- It is packaged in a tray or bowl in which it can be cooked, usually with some sort of sleeve or box around it.
- It can be either raw or cooked.
- It can be of any ethnic origin – traditional British, Indian, Chinese, American, etc.

1.5 The Emergence of "Lifestyle" Ranges

Ready meals are a relatively low-involvement product, compared, for example, with categories such as skin care products. Consumers attach a great deal of importance to the purchase decision for this type of product, and will spend a great deal of time choosing a product that fulfils their needs and their own personal image – the classic example of "selling hope in a jar".

However, compared with most grocery categories, the purchase decision for a chilled ready meal takes consumers quite a long time – a couple of minutes on average. When consumers are buying a ready meal, they will be considering a number of factors:

- What sort of mood they are in.
- The importance of the meal occasion the purchase is for (for example, a meal for a woman and her partner is generally considered to be a more important meal occasion than tea for her and the children, and a weekend meal is more important than a mid-week meal).
- They may be searching for "something different" – variety is important to many ready meals consumers.
- Increasingly, they may want something "healthy".

Retailers are responding to consumers' desire to reflect their personality through their purchase decisions by offering "lifestyle" ranges – for example, Tesco's Finest range, and Marks & Spencer's Connoisseur and Café Specials ranges, and even all the new organic ranges.

These ranges, and in particular the Café Specials range, include not only ready meals but also other products that consumers need to create a complete meal, such as vegetables, desserts, salad, wine, bread and snacks.

Each range is targeted at different consumers; for example, Connoisseur is likely to appeal to an older consumer than Café Specials, which has quite a young image.

These ranges tend to be merchandised as a group, and, in the future, it is possible that consumers will want to go to one section in the store and find a selection of products that match their own self-image or "lifestyle".

This type of approach also allows supermarkets to differentiate themselves, in a time when both quality and pricing across the chains are converging.

1.6 Home Meal Replacement (HMR)

1.6.1 The HMR market

One of the most recent developments in the ready meals market is home meal replacement. HMR can be defined as:

> "Complete meals or meal components that are freshly prepared, out of the home, and which are purchased by the consumer to eat at home, on the same day.'

HMR is developing in the States in response to consumers' desire for something more wholesome than fast food. It is being driven by foodservice operators and is seen by consumers as an alternative to eating out. In the UK, the market is being developed by the major grocery retailers, and is seen more as an alternative to preparing food at home. The types of product available in the UK include ethnic ranges such as curries, traditional pub type meals and rotisserie.

1.6.2 What exactly is a home meal replacement product?

There is a lot of similarity between chilled ready meals and home meal replacement products, but HMR products can be differentiated in several ways:

- Chilled ready meals are prepared out of the home, and are most likely to be purchased for keeping as a "standby" in the refrigerator. HMR products are also prepared out of the home, but they are for consumption generally at home or at work, on the day that they are purchased. The food is pre-prepared, but may require finishing touches at home, in addition to re-heating.

- HMR products offer significant benefits over chilled ready meals in terms of quality and presentation. They are perceived as fresher than ready meals, and consumers may assume that they are prepared on the premises. The purchase experience is closer to going to a restaurant or takeaway than a supermarket.
- HMR products are more likely to be flexible in terms of portion size, to meet the consumer's needs more closely than a chilled ready meal.

1.6.3 Who is the HMR consumer?

Because the HMR concept is so new, there is not yet a typical consumer.

In its current form, HMR probably appeals particularly to those who live alone, who are less motivated to cook for one, but still want a 'proper' meal. There has been steady growth in single-person households, which now account for around 28% of all households. Single-person households are forecast to become the major demographic group within the next few years, overtaking two-person households, which currently account for around 33% of total UK households.

HMR may also appeal to those living in multiple occupation households, such as students and young flat sharers.

A third group likely to find HMR useful is the elderly, who are also less likely to feel inclined or able to cook.

1.6.4 Why is the HMR market developing?

All the trends leading to the rapid growth of the ready meals market will also benefit the HMR market. One important trend is the increasing tendency for families to eat separately. For example, working adults are less likely to eat with the rest of the family, and, on average, teenagers eat their evening meal with the family only every other day. Also, one-third of working adults usually eat their meal without the rest of the household.

Time pressure is also increasing – the average working week in the UK is 44 hours, the longest in Europe.

Consumers mostly find shopping a chore – 46% of women and 51% of men don't enjoy it. The minority, 34% of women and 25% of men, actually enjoy it. This means that many consumers may want to get the shopping done as quickly as possible, and what could be quicker than grabbing a pre-prepared meal from a handy counter near the entrance to the shop?

1.6.5 How are HMR products delivered to consumers?

The major retailers are experimenting to find the best ways to offer their consumers home meal replacement products. The methods being used at the moment include the following:

- In-store restaurants and coffee shops, which are now in most larger stores.
- Hot snack counters.
- Self-service salad bars.
- Made to order, high quality hot and cold sandwiches.
- Bagged meal deals, such as curry, rice and naan bread. These are generally very successful, and are being rolled out across the retailers.
- Broadened deli counter offering, including meals to take home and reheat. These are also being rolled out across the retailers.

Asda has been successfully running its Curry Pot service for a number of years, and it also offers made to order and pre-made pizza. Hot and cold meal centres are now running in the stores in Canterbury, Eastleigh and Leeds, offering food for consumption at home and in-store. Asda is also experimenting with a drive-through service.

Sainsbury's has around 23 rotisserie and hot meat counters, and a similar number of curry bars.

Savacentres also offer this service, and different concepts are being trialled at the store in Calcot, including Indian, Italian and Mexican, plus fresh salads.

Tesco has a large number of rotisserie counters, and is trialling other concepts, such as curry and sushi bars. Tesco Extras has a food court in the middle of the store, providing hot meals for immediate consumption.

Retailers are now starting to look not only at individual categories within the store, but how they relate to each other. They are looking at how they can gain additional impulse sales by putting associated or "treat" products next to certain products. For example, lager, poppadoms and mango chutney next to Indian ready meals are likely to increase the consumer's spend. And how about putting videos next to them as well? Further examples include retailers' ranges such as Tesco Finest, Marks & Spencer Connoisseur, Sainsbury's Special Selection, and the new Organic ranges, all of which are generally merchandised in blocks that cut across the traditional product category definitions.

1.7 The Future

We have already mentioned two possible directions that the ready meals market might move in. We may be so short of time and cooking skills that we rely completely on pre-prepared meals bought from our local supermarket, or delivered directly to our homes.

Or we may start to rebel against processed food – after the recent spate of food scares, consumers have been becoming more aware of what they are eating. If this happens, it could give the HMR market a big boost, as consumers see these products as being fresher and more natural than ready meals.

The growth of the HMR market will mean changes to the way in which stores merchandise their prepared foods. Alternative approaches include a section within the store; an add-on facility to superstores; a stand-alone facility, independent of the supermarket; or home delivery.

So far, offering consumers HMR products does not generally seem to have adversely affected the ready meals market, and in fact it looks as though chilled ready meals sales rise when a store introduces an HMR offer. Retailers are therefore likely to address this market enthusiastically if it offers a means of developing incremental sales, as the retailers' core market is now mature and offers limited growth opportunities; over the last 10 years, the market grew by only 2.7% a year after inflation, and most of this growth was achieved through new store openings.

The foodservice market is growing as the trend towards eating out continues. Of every £1 spent on food, we now spend 30p on food out of the home (source: Office for National Statistics). It is forecast that we will spend more on eating food prepared out of the home than on food prepared in the home within the next 20 years. We are also demanding ever more convenient products to cope with our hectic lifestyles, and are beginning to see eating out as more of a regular activity than a treat.

The retailers are ideally placed to take advantage of this trend. Consumers have a great deal of trust in the big retailers, and they are already using supermarkets for products for immediate consumption, such as the lunchtime sandwich. The major retailers have very strong brand names – it has been said that people trust supermarkets more than banks! This also means that they may trust their supermarket more than the local takeaway.

The retailers will also gain if, when consumers enter a store for HMR products, they also buy other goods while they are there.

So it looks as though, in the longer term, consumers may regularly pop into their local supermarket for HMR products to eat that evening, and take chilled or frozen ready meals home to have in the fridge as a standby.

1.8 Summary

To answer the question, "what is a ready meal", we have considered a number of factors, including:

- Ingredients
- Packaging
- Storage – chilled, frozen or ambient
- Pre-cooked or raw
- Quality
- Where the product is purchased
- The development of HMR

We have also looked at why consumers buy ready meals:

- Increasingly hectic and fragmented lifestyles
- Desire for convenience
- Ease of preparation
- Greater status of evening meals compared with lunch

These factors suggest why consumers are buying more and more pre-prepared food. Sales of basic raw ingredients such as meat, bacon, oils and fats, flour, milk, cheese, eggs and sugar have been falling for some years (source: Office for National Statistics). Eventually, therefore, we may find that virtually all the food we buy is pre-prepared in some way, and ready meals and HMR are likely to be a growing part of this trend.

We have defined a ready meal in terms of the factors listed above, but the definition is likely to continue to evolve, perhaps to encompass a wide range of convenience foods, as time passes – after all, the first ready meals started out as frozen TV dinners and dried packet meals.

2. THE DEVELOPMENT PROCESS

Vicky Nolan

2.1 Introduction

New and improved ready meal products are constantly in demand in an ever-changing, dynamic and competitive marketplace.

This chapter concentrates on the development process and discusses how to develop a product with regard to relevant thoughts and considerations at each stage of the development process. Following these guidelines will ensure a considered and structured approach.

The development process is often similar for many different products and categories, but specific points relating to ready meals are highlighted.

To understand the development process involved with developing a new product, it is first essential to know who the customer is and what his or her interests are in ready meals.

For some customers, the price and value of a product are the most essential factors; for some it may be the size of the product and for others the quality. Often it can be all three. In most cases, choice is very important, and a range of different cuisines, flavours, tastes and textures will provide interest and lead to repeat purchase.

In many cases, all the above points are important, as customers are both discerning and demanding, largely because ready meals have become well established since the early 1980s, and in many cases have replaced home cooking.

2.2 Customer Need

Interest in ready meals has become an area for retailers and manufacturers that is often considered to be the fashion end of many previously longer established areas. Ready meals have become established owing to lifestyle changes, and often lead the way in trends that later become established in more mature areas, e.g. grocery – long-life products.

Customer needs vary depending on:

- Who they are – individuals, couples or families and whether they are young or more mature.
- Where they live – regionality has a large effect on the popularity of different flavours and cuisines.
- Time available.
- Importance of convenience.
- Meal occasion – everyday or special occasion, and/or time of day to be eaten. Whether the food is to be eaten in a hurry, 'on the hoof' or in a more relaxed situation, at the table, in front of a screen (TV of PC) or when entertaining.
- Different tastes, likes and dislikes – a good variety of different cuisines is essential, such as Italian and British, together with a combination of traditional and basic meals, and modern and fashionable ideas, in order to provide balance and interest.
- Choice within ranges, such as:
  - proteins
  - sauces – light or rich
  - styles of preparation
  - flavours – popular and fashionable
  - portion sizes
  - price points
- Expectation and awareness – previous knowledge of products and awareness of preparation, presentation and delivery will affect choice and repeat purchase. Therefore, products must suit the customer and their outside supermarket experiences, i.e. media, travel and eating out.
- Frequency of purchase – determining whether purchase is long-life, frozen or chilled.

2.3 The Development Process

The development process is made up of a number of stages, which will vary in their format and sometimes order, depending on who the manufacturer/retailer is and the type of ready meal involved – chilled, frozen or long-life. Generally, however, the process can be simplified into three key areas:

- Research and finalising of concepts
- Planning and developing products
- Finalising and delivering developments

When all three key stages are grouped together, the whole is identified as the development process or critical path. Interestingly, some views suggest that the critical path starts only once a product has been agreed in principle. However, the whole process is a logical sequence of events that are critical in how they are planned both in organisational and communication terms.

Ready meals, particularly when chilled, can be developed fairly quickly if necessary but, ideally, from idea to customer purchase takes a minimum of about 16 weeks. The process is often referred to as a critical process as there are key areas that must occur at set stages. The process can only be speeded up when little innovation is involved and a product very similar to a previous one is to be launched.

Producing ready meals that fill gaps, either in the market place or within a range, can take time if key areas such as quality or price points need to be considered. However innovation with ready meals can take more time at every stage and this needs to be planned for. If the process is rushed, particularly when aiming to achieve quality, innovation or a real point of difference, success can often be limited.

Above all, whose responsibility is it to drive the development process? Some believe it is the responsibility of the retailer, and others, the responsibility of the manufacturer; however, for effective results and good working relationships, it should be a two-way process driven by both parties, who both have the ultimate customer in common.

However, it is important to highlight that the roles of the retailer and the manufacturer in the development process are very different. The retailer generally sees the whole picture, and dictates it; the manufacturer is more involved in the detail and sees only the part of the picture that follows and actions the process.

At each key stage of the development cycle, both parties should be aware of the needs of the other and be communicating and exchanging ideas regularly.

Figure 2.1 provides an outline of the key stages of the development process, and Fig. 2.2 presents a development planning calendar, as a guide and example of planning the above process over a period of time.

2.3.1 Research and finalising of concepts

2.3.1.1 Researching the market and identifying trends

The approach taken on research depends on how far the of range of choice has been developed in the ready-meal offer to the customer. In small, limited offers, research will be confined initially to gap analysis and filling the needs of the specific customer profile in the particular store. In a large ready-meal offer, development will include the above but will generally lean more heavily on innovation.

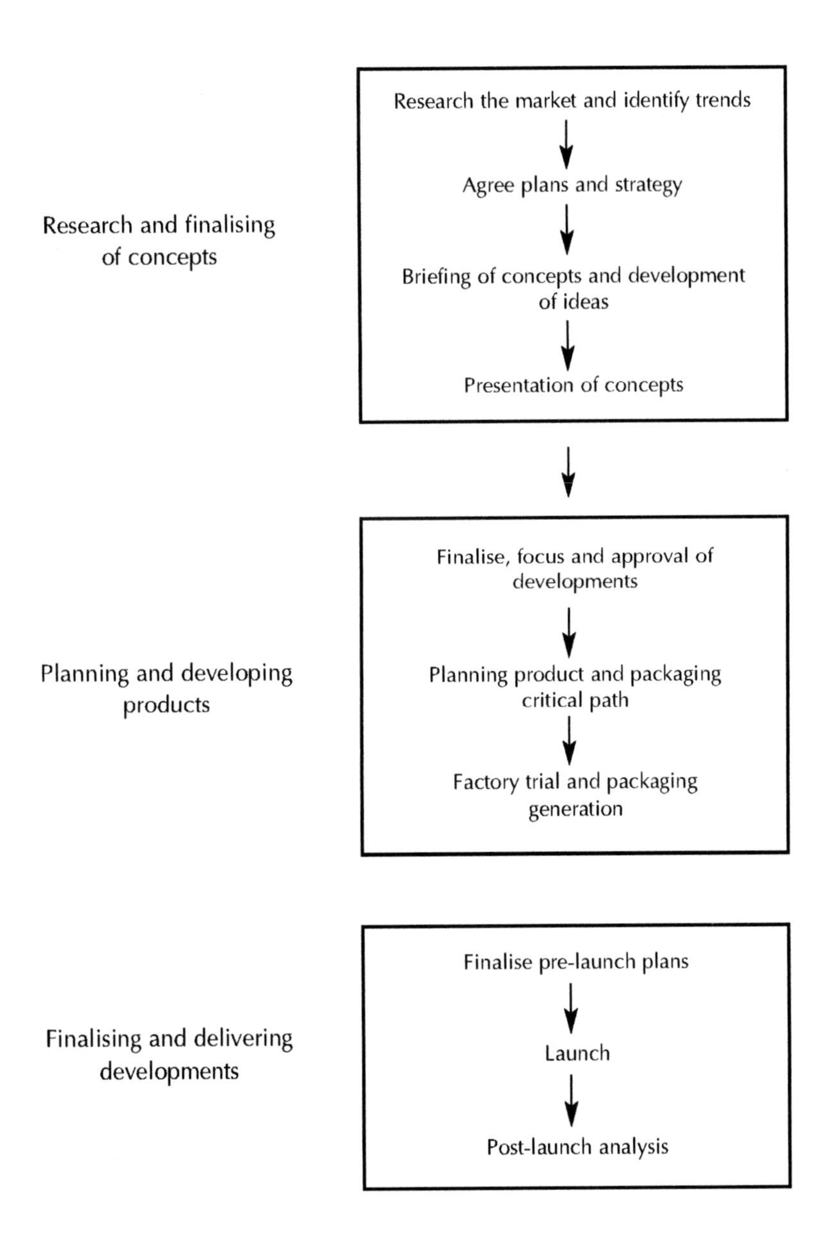

Fig. 2.1. Key stages of the development process

	January	February	March	April	May	June	July	August	September	October	November	December
AUTUMN	Research	Research	Agree plans	Manufacturer's own presentations		Finalise and approve	Factory trials			Product launches		
			Agree briefs	Manufacturer to retailer presentations		Planning meeting and critical path	Packaging generation					
SPRING			Product launches			Research		Agree plans	Manufacturer's own presentations		Finalise and approve	
								Agree briefs	Manufacturer to retailer presentations		Planning meeting and factory trials	
CHRISTMAS	Research	Manufacturer / supplier presentations	Retailer approval	Planning meeting					Factory trials		Product launches	
	Compile list of concepts											

A similar timescale needs to be given to specific/special targeted launches of "ready meals" to suit peak sales periods, e.g. Easter, World Cup finals.

Fig. 2.2. Development planning calendar

In ready meals, as with many other product areas, research for development falls under the following areas:

- Improvements to existing products
- Additions to existing groups of products
- Innovation of new areas

Ideas come from a range of sources and often from an ongoing process, not confined to set periods.

2.3.1.1.1 Market information

Establishing market information involves the following steps:-

- Competitive and own-range analysis of gaps and sales
- Brand and own-label comparisons
- Consumer research
- Benchmarking and sampling

2.3.1.1.2 Awareness of changes and developments

Awareness of trends in the market can be acquired through various channels and should encompass several different aspects of food production and sales:-

- At exhibitions – UK and worldwide
- Catering trends – both restaurants and takeaways, UK and worldwide
- New and popular ingredients
- Changing methods of food preparation and presentation
- New legislation and environmental issues
- New packaging trends
- Within the media
  - food programmes on TV and radio
  - articles in the press (papers and magazines) both national and trade
- Trends in current and new recipe books

2.3.1.1.3 Other points to consider

- Previous launches – successes and failures
- Seasonal variations/opportunities and sales balance
- Manufacturing base – skills, capacity investments and newcomers
- Pricing structure
- Portion sizes
- Overall image and customer packaging use – do they meet and suit current trends?

When developing ready meals, there always needs to be a balance if choice is to be offered, between basic well-recognised products and new, innovative ideas, to create regular repeat purchase, volume and interest. To maintain this balance:

- Protect current products/ranges with elimination of slow sellers/out-of-date concepts or improve where sales and perception are poor but concept is right for the customer.
- Add, to identified gaps in existing ranges, more up-to-date products or larger or smaller sizes of proven popular fast sellers.
- Then innovate.

2.3.1.2 Building a ready meal range

Historically, ready meals were grouped under cuisine types, i.e. Indian, Chinese, vegetable, Italian, American, British, etc. More recently, eating trends have been grouped together, such as vegetarian; 'lite' or healthy options; snack meals; organic; or premium. Some areas have become so successful that the style of preparation or a particular protein constituent is singled out as a group in its own right, e.g. casseroles or fish dinners.

2.3.1.2.1 General themes

Within any range, there are often general themes that break down the range under certain headings:

- Types of protein (beef, chicken, pork, etc.)
- Method of preparation (roast, casserole, etc.)
- Portion size – various sizes of the same product if fast selling
- Price points – various but strategic
- Different sauces (gravy, tomato-based, béchamel, etc.)

Often, ideas cross over; while the above would be a good breakdown for a cuisine-based range, e.g. Italian, for an eating trend such as vegetarian, another heading could be fast-selling dishes from different cuisines, e.g. vegetable lasagne.

When building a range, listing out headings to identify gaps always helps.

Portion sizes and price points are generally determined by the product popularity and meal occasion. Often, with ready meals, it is easier to start with a single portion and make larger sizes later. However, if it is not a complete eat, for example, braised steak and gravy, then it may be better to have this as a 'serves two' product, where the inconvenience of adding vegetables to make a complete meal is less of an issue. Single portions often do better if they are complete meals, since those eating them usually want the convenience of time saving.

Equally, larger portions work well if they offer real convenience by saving preparation time and/or are a product customers may not have the skill to prepare themselves.

2.3.1.2.2 Current trends

Current trends affect both existing and new products and need to be considered when building a range. Trends to consider are:

- Cuisines – popular and new
- Style of preparation
- Raw materials/flavours – popular and new

All the above are affected by lifestyle/eating habits, income, fashions, different age group requirements, new technical developments and media coverage.

Ways to identify trends include eating out in a cross-section of restaurants, talking to people involved with food, and observing what is happening in other parts of the world.

In the past, ready meals became established initially as branded products in both long-life and frozen sectors, but only on a very limited scale. It was not until the chilled-ready-meal boom that the market took off and became far more recognised. Nowadays, most developments generally start as a concept in the chilled area and, if successful, they become adapted into frozen and long-life sectors.

2.3.1.2.3 Other points to consider

Developing a product within a range must include other considerations:

- Who is the customer; what are their outside expectations and experiences; what are they looking for – price and value, quality or quantity?
- What should the product be like? Benchmark against other retailers' products, specialist shops and chef/home-produced products.
- What is the best and is this necessary to know? If it is necessary, experience it by eating in well-recognised restaurants, talking to experts and travelling to the country of origin.

- Should the product be authentic or anglicised? Often this is answered by customer expectations and experience based on where they will have come across the particular product. This can also be affected by palate differences; for example, salty ingredients that are popular in one country will not be as acceptable in the UK as we tend to prefer creamy, less salty flavours owing to our dairy history. In mature markets, both anglicised and authentic products can usually be offered. In new areas, direction will be led by customer experiences, not necessarily experiences of the retailer or manufacturer.
- What is the intended use of the product? – i.e. meal centre – complete or accompaniment?
- What type of packaging is needed to give the required end use?
- What image is needed to reflect the price, meal occasion and product style?
- What are the appropriate raw materials and processes required to produce a successful result?
- What equipment is needed to produce the product? Does it require adapting or is investment needed?
- Agree portion size, weight and price point. Should this fall in line with other similar weights and prices?
- If necessary, how will the product be reheated by the customer? Is microwaveability necessary? Are time and speed of importance? Or should the choice be left to the customer?

Development research will vary depending on whether existing areas are being improved or added to, or whether innovation and new areas are needed.

Improvements and additions are generally identified through low sales, customer feedback, benchmarking and sampling, and market research. Points to consider include:

- Product formulation – raw material/process changes to simplify and modernise.
- Improvement of both portion size and price points into a simplified clearly thought through strategy to meet current customer demands.
- Is there any new legislation requiring alterations?
- Have the correct raw materials been used for the required end result? Are there obvious missing ingredients or unnecessary additions?

- Does the eating quality of the kitchen-produced product differ considerably when compared with the factory-produced product? Are the ingredients over-processed?
- Should new suppliers be used for raw materials?
- Is the correct manufacturer being used to produce the product, i.e. are the wrong process controls being used to produce the product or is there insufficient capacity/investment to meet sales demand?

With all the research and information gathered, the direction of development should be followed in a logical order by considering the following:

- Sales information
- Market information
- Current range – eating quality
  – portion size/price
- Newness

2.3.1.3 Agreement of plans and strategy

At this stage the priorities are agreed and the research collated under headings:

- Market – gaps and opportunities
- Trends – cuisines; styles and flavours
- Eating habits – meal occasions
- Raw materials – established and new
- Processing methods – established and new
- Packaging trends – presentation and innovation
- Portion-size requirements
- Pricing structures
- Seasonal and regional variations
- Lessons learnt from previous launches – both successful and unsuccessful

The conclusions obtained are used to establish:

- Customer requirements
- Number of improvements
- Number of additions
- Products to eliminate
- Amount of innovation
- Capacity and investment
- Resource

This, in turn, directs strategy and plans for:

- Priorities and balance between improvements, additions and innovations
- Timescale
- Number of products
- When to launch through the year
- Price and portion policy

2.3.1.4 Giving and receiving the brief

The selection of a manufacturer needs careful consideration to ensure that their skills and capacity are understood, and understanding needs checking both ways.

The briefing stage is vital if all the research and priorities of development are to be well understood. Briefs need to be flexible to allow for changes in the market, covering trends and corporate policies.

The brief can be given verbally but should always be supported in writing to avoid any misunderstanding. Information needed should come under the following headings:

- Product – with key attributes
- Category/range status
- Target customer and consumer need
- Competitive status – state advantages against competitors
- Benchmark, if relevant
- Target price
- Meat content/legal considerations
- Target weight
- Target launch
- Full product description – flavour, appearance, texture and packaging format

The response to a brief will need additional information, including:

- Projected volume
- Shelf life of product
- Legislation and claims
- Critical path/timescale

2.3.1.5 Development of ideas

After a brief has been received, sufficient time needs to be given for working on the products (ideally 3-4 weeks) prior to presentations. Products often have to be made a number of times before the correct results are achieved. How is this process conducted and what are the general rules?

2.3.1.5.1 Developing a recipe

- Always start with the ultimate and most authentic product. Make this with all the correct ingredients and to the correct process, as an initial benchmark and guide.
- Adapt recipe where necessary – depending on customer awareness and price considerations. Always adapt from the ultimate product, never adapt from a compromise. Raw materials and/or the process may need to be altered but always aim to keep as close to the authentic as possible.
- Gather together raw materials from approved materials and/or new ones that will need approval. Wherever possible, use ingredients from the factory to avoid complications later on.
- Weigh and record everything accurately. Record percentage content of ingredients in addition to weights, as this can be used subsequently for increasing batch sizes in initial factory trials and final production.
- Make reports as necessary if levels/amounts of ingredients and/or the cooking methods are changed.
- Record yields; this is vital information when the process is transferred from the kitchen to the factory.

This stage of the development process is carried out by development kitchen staff/chefs. Early involvement of factory commercial and technical personnel is also advisable to avoid any issues that may slow down the process later on.

Pack weights, packaging ideas and initial costings are also done at this stage.

2.3.1.6 Presentation of products and ranges

It is vital that the products presented are justified against the original brief, whether presentations are given by manufacturers or by other sources in a formal or informal way.

A list highlighting the following information should be provided at this stage:

- Percentage content of individual ingredients
- Ingredients suppliers

- Quality/type of ingredient
- Method of processing, in a simplified format
- Yields
- Make-up weights and declared weights
- Re-heating/cooking instructions
- Shelf life
- Proposed packaging

Additional information should include:

- Investment required to go national
- Cost of product, with breakdown of ingredients, labour and packaging costs

The following should also be considered at this stage:

- Any technical issues that need to be raised
- Recipe formulations and raw materials availability
- Comparisons with similar-style products or products in the market place, particularly in key areas such as price, weight and meat content, etc.
- Decisions regarding packaging; concepts should be shown by the manufacturer or, in some cases, instigated by the retailer

  Consider:

  - pack style to suit product price and use
  - awareness of costs of different materials, off the shelf or make-up costs;
    sleeves or boxes
  - lead-times for packaging
  - shapes and sizes, i.e. will the product fit the pack, does it look too empty or too full, or could it leak?
  - image and photography; the accuracy of the image (being honest to the customer) is vital – never include more in the photograph than is in the product
  - is the pack suitable for transportation home by the customer, storage and reheating/cooking.

In taste-testing, ideally, no more than 10 to 12 products should be presented in a single session. Bland flavours should be sampled first and spicy flavours last. Sufficient product for sampling should be served:

- cold and heated in the packaging

- as a complete, heated portion on a serving dish, to assess size and customer target

2.3.2 Planning and developing products

2.3.2.1 Finalising, focus and approval of developments

From all the products presented, the retailer (NPD or buyer) will make the final decisions and selection of the developments. He needs to ensure that his choice is well focused and offers:

- choice in produce type
- choice in price and portion sizes
- choice in improvements, additions and innovation/newness
- choice in packaging styles/presentation
- choice for meal occasions

It is important not to over-duplicate in any area where less choice could yield more in return. In new ranges, four products are often better than six; too many should not be selected simply because you can't decide which to choose – i.e. do not hope that the customer will do this for you! This is inefficient and wastes time and money; a decision must be made.

The following need to be agreed and approved at this stage before proceeding:

- margins
- distribution – short and long term
- packaging
- store delivery in trays, boxes, etc.

This approval process can take place through discussions, presentations or both. When presenting meals in ranges, always start with improvements, followed by additions, and end on a high with innovations.

2.3.2.2 Plan product and packaging critical path

Good communication with all concerned (i.e. at retailer – buyer, NPD and technical, and at manufacturer – NPD; marketing, commercial, production and technical) will result in fast effective delivery. Everyone involved needs to be aware of the approved products and, if necessary, products may need to be sampled again. Agreement needs to be reached with everyone on quality issues, constraints, safety issues and timescales.

A series of meetings needs to take place to establish plans for:

- Launch programme targeting correct season and region, if necessary
- Critical path for development and design of packaging – this process can often take longer than the time to produce a good product
- Agreeing cover for trials
- Reviewing technical priorities:
  - key product attributes
  - formulation
  - raw materials/process
  - discuss any issues
- Factory implications:
  - capacity and environmental issues
  - training and recruitment
  - new procedures
  - impact on current production
- Commercial considerations:
  - promotional and marketing plans
  - volume estimates
  - financial targets

Figure 2.3 presents a packaging and product critical path and timescale example.

2.3.2.3 Transfer of product from kitchen to factory

Involvement up to this stage has largely been done by development, with some buying/commercial and technical input. However, once the retailer has approved the products, the manufacturer needs to start the transfer from kitchen to factory as quickly as possible. In some cases, this may already have happened if there are any doubts whether the product can be made in production.

Handing over from kitchen to factory is handled differently by different manufacturers, but a good understanding of the kitchen-approved product is vital, and the product must have been sampled by those involved in production first. It is important to have a kitchen-approved product available at all times to sample against for appearance, flavour, texture and aroma.

Timescale in weeks	Product critical path	Design and packaging critical path
	Research market	
	Agree plans	
This can be up to a 5-month period	Brief concepts	Source and start to tool up new packaging formats
	Presentation of concepts	
	Finalise and approve concepts	
	Planning product and packaging critical path	
0	Approve kitchen and initial costings	
2		Collect design information
3	Factory trials	Brief design
4-5		Design concepts
6-7		Finalise design
8	Final factory product approval and confirm costs	Start artwork photography/illustrations and cooking instructions
10	Pre-production	Artwork/chromalin to repro house
13	Finalise all pre-launch and store plans	Approve wet proofs
14-15		Films to printer Printing and packaging delivery
16	LAUNCH	

Fig. 2.3. Packaging and product critical path and timescale

Various difficulties can be experienced in transfer:

- Bulking up a recipe can alter characteristics dramatically – weights, ingredients and sometimes methods need to be adjusted.
- Using equipment that is not suited to the desired end result can present limitations; without foresight, this can sometimes stop a good idea from proceeding.
- Inability to use ingredients that were used in the development kitchen, either because they are too costly or cannot be obtained from a suitable approved source, can obviously affect the end result.

2.3.2.4 Factory trials and packaging generation

It often is useful for the retailer (NPD generally) to have a checklist by product or category of product to ensure that every stage of the factory trials and packaging priorities is covered. The checklist will vary depending on the manufacturer, retailer and type of product (chilled, frozen or long-life) and the specific constraints followed for each. However, general points covered should include:

- Confirm recipe
- Agree raw materials/sources
- Review process
- Conduct consumer panels
- Approve kitchen product
- Agree initial costings
- Draft specification
- Brief packaging and design
- Factory trials
- Request cooking instructions
- Draw up product attributes
- Photography
- Travel test
- Shelf life
- Nutritional information
- Approve designs
- Start artwork
- Approve factory trial and costings
- Artwork to repro
- Reproduction
- Approve proofs
- Printing date
- Packaging design

- First production
- Finalise launch plans
- Launch date

During trials, it is important to ensure that the original kitchen-receipt is watched and used as a benchmark.

Weights, speeds, timings and all controls need to be followed and recorded, and all factory operators trained to understand the quality standards to be achieved. It is also important to check that methods to produce consistency have been set up.

Some of the problems that can occur at this stage in the ready meal process include:

- Use, or planned use, of too many batch sizes, resulting in variation in quality.
- Incorrect weighing and yielding.
- Process or timings not followed accurately.
- Too much "colflo" (used to thicken sauces to make them freeze-stable) resulting in a glue-like consistency and dulled flavours.
- Poor distribution of major components.
- Flavour enhancers used instead of cooking the ingredients correctly to develop their flavour, e.g. mushrooms.
- Incorrect maturity of cheese or meat used, affecting flavour and succulence.
- Not being true to original kitchen process and/or taking short cuts, resulting in a drop in quality standards.

2.3.2.4.1 Design and packaging

- Designs for ready meals packaging need to reflect the meal occasion and pricing structure. Simple low-cost products require a very different look from a premium high-cost ready meal.
- Designs for different ranges need a common modern feel but also need to reflect their individual characteristics.
- Use of colours is important:
  - One common colour or group of colours for a range creates a clear identity and impact on display but can also create difficulty in individual product identification.

  - Equally, different colours for each product overcomes this issue but lacks boldness and clarity on displays.
  - Use colours that work together at distances – white out of yellow as a typescript is difficult to read at a distance.
- Titles need to be clearly understood by customers and subtitles should only highlight key attributes and not become an ingredient list. Question when it will work to use authentic product names and when an English translation will be better understood.
- Above all, designs need to be kept up to date, be modern and have integrity.
- Photography needs to be clear and accurate – a product is being sold and it is not necessary to create inspiration or a mood as in a magazine. It is wise to attend photographic sessions to ensure that the product is accurately represented. For this reason, factory samples should be used for these shoots and not kitchen-produced products.
- Packaging must work for the consumer for transportation and reheating/ cooking.
- Check all details on the artwork – nutritional, ingredients and cooking instructions. Include any special selling features/messages to help attract the consumer – but not too many to cause confusion.
- At proof stage, get others to check – do not rely on just one individual – it is easy to miss small things such as spelling mistakes.

Apart from weight and price, the packaging and design are the first things that a consumer is confronted with in the store. Insufficient time spent on image can often affect sales and success of an otherwise excellent product.

2.3.3 Finalising and delivering developments

2.3.3.1 Finalising pre-launch plans

All quality issues and all technical and commercial priorities must be agreed.

It is vital to target products at the right time of year and keep to timescales. If either of these is not followed, for whatever reason, the success of a product can be badly affected.

2.3.3.2 Launch and post-launch analysis

- Approve products for distribution.

- Meet regularly in first few weeks to ensure that standards are being met consistently.
- Monitor quality against any increased production.
- Keep a list of products launched over each development season or over the course of a year. Note any delistings and reasons.
- Look for patterns and trends:
  - popular raw materials, e.g. chicken
  - popular preparations
  - popular price points, etc.

Use this information when planning future ready meals.

A new product launch can result in an unsuccessful outcome for various reasons, and questions need to be answered to explain the situation:

- Was the product understood by the customer and was it what the customer expected; was it too authentic or too anglicised?
- Did it represent good value or was the price too high? How did it compare with other retailers' products?
- Was the product/range marketed well or was it lost on the counter?
- Was the concept right but the manufacturing process incorrect and did not deliver the intended result?
- Was the concept too fringe and not familiar enough for the consumer?
- Was the packaging wrong for the product?
- Was the product launched at the right time of year? Did it clash with other promotions?
- Was the eating quality good enough?
- Was the product sufficiently different from other products already on the counter?

Generally, reasons for a product/range being unsuccessful are often easy to identify and are ones that occur time and again. The information obtained from an analysis can be used to try a good idea again after correcting what may have been a small and easily resolved problem.

2.4 Conclusions

Every stage in the development process is important and, when sufficient time is given to each stage, it will ensure better control of costs, resources and, ultimately, results.

It is often quicker to improve or add to existing ranges, and success is often more certain. However, if time is taken to break new ground and offer real newness, success can be far more significant and sustainable.

In reality, the period of time taken from research and concept development through to factory trial stage does not always take up to 5 months as indicated, as this is an ideal situation. Ideas and their development at a kitchen level are often ongoing and need to be when reacting to fashion and trends. Developing good and innovative ideas takes time in order to produce pleasing and consistent results. Above all, the area of ready meals is one where those involved do need to have at least a real interest in food, and a depth of food knowledge is of enormous benefit in understanding the complexity of this area.

The development process is a two-way exchange between the retailer and the manufacturer, and communication between the two parties at all times is vital. Manufacturers who keep the retailer well informed, keep to timescales and are one jump ahead on trends, innovation and sales are more likely to be favoured with developments.

3. SOURCING RAW MATERIALS

Tony McMullen

3.1 Introduction

The choice of raw materials, and suppliers that produce and sell them, is one of the most critical decisions that can be made in the production of any food product.

Whilst a quality assurance system should ensure that the desirable attributes of any product stays within an acceptable range throughout its processing, it is of little use if the raw material does not meet the starting parameters of the process.

To this end there are basically two choices:

i) **Operate quality control at intake**: This simply means that products are accepted or rejected after inspection at intake.

   This throws up a number of problems, one of which is how to feed the production department's raw material need if it is rejected. This in turn may lead to customers not receiving their full order. Clearly, both situations have a negative economic impact.

   We must also consider how many, and what kind of quality checks can be carried out in a busy intake area where raw material delivery turnarounds are likely to be very quick, and space and facilities limited.

   Control at intake, by itself, is clearly not ideal.

ii) **Operate quality assurance of raw materials**: This requires that a more global picture of the supplier, his premises and systems is assessed, as much as, if not more than the product he supplies.

   We should view the supplier/buyer relationship as a partnership. Most reputable suppliers are eager for their technical ability to be considered as part of the deal, and we should optimise our use of these facilities.

The aim should be that there are fewer rejections and a better information flow between the two companies.

If a supplier clearly understands your standards and requirements, he is likely to be considering other ways in which he can help your business and develop his own into the bargain.

In the following chapter is a practical and systematic approach, based on quality assurance, to managing the establishment of new suppliers/ingredients, which will, hopefully, minimise the costs, time and risks involved and provide 'right first time' raw materials.

Control of raw materials is essential to ensuring that each finished ready meal is safe and legal, and is achieving its optimum quality and shelf life.

3.2 Existing versus New Suppliers

'It is better the devil you know than the devil you don't' is a worthy creed; however, with the pressures upon product development departments to be ever more innovative and the pressures upon the buying departments to find cost savings it is inevitable that new suppliers must be considered.

3.2.1 Existing suppliers

Very often the safest and most reliable option is to stay with companies that have given you a reliable service, and products without incident, over many years. A credible track record cannot be overestimated.

A lot of time can be saved on both sides when they understand your needs and systems, and vice-versa. Ideally, regular updates on new opportunities and developments in areas of interest to you need to be encouraged. Initial development work, and trending quality aspects of fresh products throughout the year are paramount. If products are seasonal it is important that you are offered alternatives well in advance of the decision-making time.

Wherever possible, new ingredients should be sourced from existing suppliers.

3.2.2 New suppliers

In the dynamic arena of food processing one can never be complacent; there is always a new product to be evaluated or a new process to be reviewed and, occasionally, a new supplier that must be considered.

As a general rule, there must be a good reason for using a new supplier because the resources used in setting up a new approved supplier are considerable and the risks posed by their products are generally greater.

No matter how thoroughly you may have audited a company's systems and factory, you cannot really assess how it will deal with issues on a practical basis, when you are not there, until they arise. However, new suppliers can bring new opportunities and solutions.

3.3 Technical Back-up

If a supplier is to function as an extension to your department, which would be ideal, it is important for it to be able to offer some form of technical back-up. The supplier should be able to deal with routine testing and information flow, as well as having the facility for handling a crisis.

Ideally, it should be able to carry out your intake checks when, or before the product is despatched. This would render onsite intake checks as simply a monitor of thoroughness and an assessment of the effect of the delivery transport upon the product and packaging. Negative results discovered before despatch also cut the reaction time if the product needs to be replaced with an alternative batch. Uplifting and replacing materials that have already been provisionally accepted, i.e. pending microbiological results, takes longer, costs more, and is inconvenient to both parties.

The kind of technical back-up you might expect from producers is as follows:

i) **Certificates of analysis**: These relate to critical aspects of the ingredient delivered and should be identified by following the HACCP procedure. Aspects covered could include microbiological loading, specific bacteria, pH, a_w and chemical analysis such as fat content and meat content. Certificates of analysis should be challenged occasionally by your own testing, the frequency of the challenge testing depending upon the track record of the supplier and the sensitivity of the parameter that is being tested in the ingredient. If discrepancies are found, the challenge testing should be increased until the reason for the discrepancy is clarified and corrected.

   Bear in mind that certificates of analysis generally cover the product parameters prior to being despatched. This might be followed by a few hours on a refrigerated truck or weeks in an environment-controlled container on a ship. Whatever distribution system is being used, it may contribute to discrepancies between certificates of analysis and your challenge testing.

Certificates of conformance generally confirm that the product delivered matches the specification. Any product delivered outside the specification parameters is in breach of that agreement; therefore a certificate of conformance is simply stating the obvious and is of little use.

ii) **Laboratory**: An onsite laboratory ensures that you will get a quicker feedback on microbiology and chemical testing. When auditing, it is important to review any third party challenge testing they carry out, and whether they hold a third party accreditation, e.g. NAMAS. This gives reassurance that results should be consistent and credible.

If a third party laboratory is used it has the advantage of being completely impartial; however it does slow down the feedback of results.

iii) **Dealing with issues**: Issues come in many guises; some come with plenty of warning, in the form of well-discussed legislation, and some come with virtually no warning at all in the form of 'food scares' that require immediate action to ensure that public health is not prejudiced and public confidence can be quickly re-established for the good of your business and the industry as a whole. The key points here are to ensure that they have information gathering systems in place for pending codes of practice and legislation, full traceability and crisis management systems, which are regularly tested.

3.4 New Supplier Co-ordination

If a potential supplier has been identified, it is important that the Product Development, Buying and Technical teams work in unison in order for the company to make the most of the opportunity.

An 'Approved Supplier Register' should be drawn up by the Technical Department and issued to the Buying and Product Development teams that lists tried and trusted suppliers, what product groups they currently supply, and what other related product groups you feel they could safely supply. This will help prevent the proliferation of suppliers, which will help the Buying Department, and allow Product Development a 'shop window' from which they can select new ingredients.

If the decision is taken that an ingredient needs to be sourced from a new supplier, some basic information needs to be gleaned before extensive trial work is conducted.

It can be useful to talk to current users of a new supplier to establish a feel for the company's culture, its approach to clients and how it has dealt with issues in the past.

In the initial stages, a completed supplier questionnaire, specification and HACCP for the product in question is helpful. This will establish, at least, that the company knows what it should be doing and that it has a co-ordinated approach to product safety and quality. Specification parameters and tolerances should also be discussed and agreed at this stage.

If the supplier questionnaire is comprehensively answered, initial trials can go ahead with a measure of confidence, without a great deal of resource applied.

If trials are successful, the next step is for the buying team to establish acceptable pricing and predicted volumes that are required. If the factory is audited and approved before prices have been set, it will give the buying team less scope to negotiate.

The final step, and the one that requires the greatest resource, is to audit the factory, and systems of the supplier. This is to establish that the company is actually practising what it claimed in the supplier questionnaire, and to look into all areas in more depth.

3.5 Supplier Questionnaires

Supplier questionnaires cover initial company details plus some basic product safety risk control information that would be covered in an audit. With low-risk ingredient suppliers, approval could be based on this questionnaire, the product specification and HACCP; however, in all other cases, questionnaires should be followed up by an audit.

Suppliers should be reviewed on a regular basis because, as we are all aware, industry requirements change rapidly and changes in management can alter company culture. Each review process should be initiated by asking the company to fill in the questionnaire followed up by an audit where relevant.

Below are listed headings that should be covered, followed by some detail as to what aspects are required under each heading:

- Details of supplier: name, postal and e-mail addresses, telephone and fax numbers.
- Details of producer: name, postal and e-mail addresses, telephone and fax numbers. This may be the same as the supplier; however, the supplier may be an agent, in which case it is important that the point of production is pinpointed for this product.
- Key contacts – Sales contact: office, mobile and out-of-hours telephone numbers.
  – Technical contact: office, mobile and out-of-hours telephone numbers.

- Organisational chart: listing responsibilities, names, titles, and reporting structure.

- General information: Size of factory and site, age of factory, number of full-time and part-time employees, membership of research associations and quality accreditations (EFSIS, BRC, etc.), accreditation of laboratory used (NAMAS).

- Design/layout
  - Layout of product flow: ensure logical product flow that does not compromise the high-risk status of prepared food.
  - Monitoring of fabric: ensure that there is regular monitoring of factory fabric; this should include glass/plastic audits, pest proofing, and damage to walls and floor. It should be explained how the information is fed back and followed up.
  - Materials used in fabric: fabric of all internal floors, walls and ceilings must be impervious and durable, and corners coved.
  - Air handling: filtration levels, positive air pressure in the high-risk area, tolerance in temperature-controlled areas, extraction above cooking areas.
  - Storage areas on- and offsite: how these areas are secured and product transported to and from them.
  - Drains: are high- and low-risk systems kept separate? What controls are in place to prevent blockages and backflows?

- Housekeeping and hygiene
  - Responsibility for cleaning: who ensures clean as you go and equipment washing during production? Who deals with cleaning out of production hours? Do they employ contract cleaners?
  - Hygiene training: has the company invested in training or appointing trained people for the critical operation of cleaning? Do all staff hold the basic food hygiene certificate?

- Cleaning schedules and methods: all areas should be covered, including utensils, equipment, protective clothing, ceilings, walls, floors and perimeter.

- High-pressure hose policy: if they are used, how are they controlled to reduce the risk of aerosol contamination?

- Stock rotation: how is the stock controlled to ensure that product is used within its shelf life?

- Disposal of waste: ensure that the waste storage, exit route and disposal do not pose a contamination threat.

- Employee health checks: what health checks are carried out on employees before starting, after visiting high-risk countries and on an ongoing basis?

- Monitoring of cleaning: there should be a combination of visual checks, and swabbing for ATP, non-specific and specific bacteria, i.e. *Listeria*. *Listeria* swabbing should be carried out after cleaning but before production to ensure that the hygiene team has been effective, and during production to ensure that cross-contamination controls are effective.

- Policy on jewellery, eating and smoking: what jewellery is permitted in the production area? Does it pose a foreign body risk? Are smoking, eating and production areas suitably segregated to pose no contamination risk?

- High/low risk control: what physical controls are in place, i.e. access points, positive air pressure, and what procedural controls are in place, i.e. colour coding of clothing, changing and washing facilities?

- Pest control: is a specialist pest control company employed? How many visits per year are made by technicians and field biologists?

- Pallet control: to what extent are external pallets permitted into the factory? How are they differentiated from internal pallets?

- Processing
  - HACCP: what disciplines are in the HACCP team? How is the system kept updated in regard to new products and recipe/processing changes?
  - Metal detection: to what sensitivity is the metal detector set? How often is the calibration and rejection system checked? Who checks the metal detector calibration? How are they trained? Are the reject bins locked? Are the engineers trained to reduce the risk of metal contamination?
  - Supplier auditing: how often are they audited? Who audits them?
  - Traceability: how do they ensure complete traceability? How often is it tested?
  - Crisis management system: do they have one? Has it been tested?

3.6 Supplier Audits

If it is assumed that the Buying Department is now happy with the price and delivery schedules of the potential new supplier, and the specification, HACCP, and supplier questionnaire were acceptable, it is now time to move into the final phase and meet the people and inspect the premises.

3.6.1 Systems audits

Provided that the production premises are reasonably accessible, there should be little problem with carrying out a site audit. However, if, for example, the supplier is importing coconut milk from Sri Lanka, it might be prudent to opt for a systems audit.

A systems audit is where the agent's appraisal, auditing, and inspection systems of his suppliers and produce are tested. It should be considered if he has covered what you would review in an audit yourself.

A systems audit will never match a first-hand site audit; however, it is an option that can be considered as a practical starting point. If the systems audit finds the supplier's systems wanting in one aspect or another, then there is another set of options to consider:

i) Use another importer.
ii) Go and audit the producer yourself.
iii) Insist on improvement to the system, where it was found to be lacking.
iv) Put in a positive release system for each batch of product either at the importer's or your own site.

Which option is chosen should be guided by the risks involved with the ingredient in question, the further processing it will receive, and the faith that you have in the importer's systems. In a nutshell, assess the hazards and controls and apply a bit of common sense.

3.6.2 *Premises audits*

Don't be too surprised if you walk into a sparkling factory, with production running at a moderate speed, and packing staff looking attentive. Whilst first impressions tell you a lot, they do not generally reflect the reality of the end of the evening shift. However, a thorough audit should give a picture of what happens when you are not there.

The objective of the audit is to check three basic principles. They are:

i) Does the factory have sufficient systems to monitor and control the quality and safety of the product?
ii) Are the systems being followed?
iii) Are there records to show that the systems have been followed.

There are seven key areas that should be covered during the site visit and a number of specifics within each area should be considered.

A number of answers will already have been supplied as part of the supplier questionnaire. It is worth revisiting these to ensure that the correct picture has been portrayed.

1. Location and buildings
   a) Internal and external fabric construction and condition
   b) External problems, e.g. flooding and smells from other premises
   c) Security of access
   d) Protection of waste storage area
   e) Drain and floor cleanliness and flow direction
   f) Air temperature, filtration and high-/low-risk flow
   g) Water supply safety

2. Hygiene
   a) Cleaning schedules for all areas
   b) Hygiene monitoring
   c) Control of food, drink and smoking

d) Protective clothing and laundry facilities
e) High-/low-risk access and identification
f) Medical screening and first aid
g) Dress/jewellery control
h) Toilet facilities
i) Handwashing facilities

3. Contamination control
a) Pest control reports
b) Glass control procedures
c) Pest-proofing windows and doors
d) Metal detection procedures
e) Engineering/repair procedures

4. Raw materials control
a) Specifications
b) Intake checks
c) Hold/reject area procedures
d) Stock rotation
e) Supplier audits

5. Process control
a) Equipment condition and cleanliness
b) Equipment maintenance and calibration
c) Process documentation
d) HACCP implementation
e) Temperatures and dwell times
f) Hold/reject area procedures
g) Weight control/records
h) Packaging handling
i) Staff training
j) Labelling
k) Stock rotation
l) Traceability

6. Product quality
a) Meets agreed specification
b) Microbiological testing facilities/records
c) Chemical testing facilities/records
d) Other testing, e.g. pesticides
e) Positive release procedures
f) Certificates of analysis
g) Tasting procedures
h) Corrective actions

7. Social trading aspects (depending upon the country)
   a) Safe working environment
   b) Elements of fair trade
   c) Sufficient remuneration
   d) No discrimination (sex, religion, etc.)
   e) No child labour

3.7 Specifications

Samples sent for initial trials will generally be accompanied by a product data sheet. However, it is important that more product information is available in order to ensure that any valid segregation procedures can be implemented, i.e. meat or nuts, and that it does not breach any 'site free' agreement that may have been agreed with the customer, e.g. GMO risk ingredients. Otherwise, there is a risk of contaminating other products or putting a lot of resource into developing a product that might come to naught.

To this end it would be useful to request a supplier specification for any sample that is sent, so that any issues about the ingredient can be addressed at the start.

By and large, ingredients specifications are informative. They will usually serve to weed out any major concerns at the initial trial phase, and give a starting point to discuss any issues that may be unclear.

However, before the launch of a product, the supplier should fill out, and sign, a specification in your own format. This should cover general issues, which are likely to be covered in the supplier's specification, as well as issues that are specific to your site and client, which may not be covered by the supplier's specification.

The issues that should be covered in your own format are as follows:

- Product name: this ensures that you use the same name for the product, so there should be no confusion when communicating with the supplier.

- Identity code: there may be a number of different grades of the product. The ID code should give absolute clarity as to the product and grade required. Both sides should be aware of the coding used and what it refers to.

- Revision number: if the product is used for any length of time, there will be revisions to the specification occasionally due to new legal requirements, your request, or routine reviews by the supplier. It is important that both parties refer to the same specification issue.

- Date of issue: this will indicate when a specification might need reviewing and possibly updating.

- Supplier signature: formally indicates that the supplier accepts the contents of the specification.
- Client signature: formally indicates that you accept the contents of the specification.
- Supplier address, contact and contact numbers: in order for you to know whom to contact with reference to the specification.
- Producer address, contact and contact numbers: in case the producer is different from the supplier and you want to contact him directly.
- Country of origin: confirms whether the product was produced in Britain, a country in the EU, or elsewhere. This can be a useful tool in marketing (e.g. pasta from Italy) and when dealing with food issues originating from a specific country. It also indicates what legislative constraints would have been put on its production.
- Method of manufacture: allows a review of possible risks inherent in the system.
- Reference to HACCP: confirms that HACCP has been addressed and how it fits into the method of manufacture.
- Reference to transport: this should confirm an undertaking to deliver product in hygienic conditions, which are temperature-controlled where relevant.
- Allergen information: extremely important for labelling purposes. It is important that it is possible to indicate components that people might be allergic to, or choose to eat or avoid for ethical, dietary or other reasons.

Table 3.I lists 18 different kinds of component that could be indicated as a presence or absence in the raw material. From this, a balanced decision can be made as to what should be declared on the finished product label. To be on the safe side any derivative of a component should be classified as the component for this exercise. The list is not exhaustive and some items on the list (e.g. nuts) have subgroups of their own.

TABLE 3.I
Possible types of components in raw materials for ready meals

Gluten	Nuts	Fish
Maize	Milk	Chicken
Maize identity preserved	Lactose	Kosher
Soya	Organic	Halal
Soya identity preserved	Offal	Dairy
Egg	Meat	Wheat

- Product composition: a list of components in descending order of content in the product will help in the formulation of a final product ingredient declaration.
- Labelling declaration: what the company believes is the legal definition of this ingredient on a finished product label.
- Storage life: necessary for ordering cycles and capacity planning.
- Storage conditions: necessary for capacity planning of the environment required, i.e. freezer, chiller or warehousing.
- Product packaging and labelling: it is important that the intake staff knows if the product is going to arrive in a 1,000-litre tank or 10-litre buckets. Packaging should be sealed and of a different colour from the product that it contains, generally blue. The label should have reference to the use-by date, product name, weight/volume, storage instructions and traceability code.
- Nutritional information: helpful when trying to compose a product with a specific dietary claim.
- Microbiological specification: particularly important if the ingredient is going to be added directly into the finished product without processing.
- Chemical specification: meat content, fat content, free fatty acid, etc. This is quite product-specific.
- Positive release: it should be clarified if the product is to be positively released by the supplier, what testing it will be positively released on, and whether the results of the test need to be communicated to you.
- Other quality test parameters: the test should be followed by the tolerance permitted, the frequency tested and the method used. Checks such as metal detection, weights and temperatures would fall into this category.
- Organoleptic evaluation: some reference should be made to what the product should look, taste and smell like.

3.8 Seasonality

One of the problems with using fresh raw materials is that they have a short shelf life. Therefore, they often cannot be positively released, and quality can vary depending upon the time of year, the weather and market demands.

Whilst meat and dairy products are relatively consistent throughout the year, a good deal of thought should be given to potential supply if a product is being designed to use fresh fish or vegetables. An obvious solution would be to use frozen products. This would allow a more consistent supply, price and quality; however, there is an undeniable quality premium when fresh components are used, so rather than avoiding the challenge it is better to look into how to manage it.

Fish variety, quantities, quality and price will depend upon the breeding cycle, location, EU quotas, and weather allowing the boats to get out to fish. However, for the rest of this illustration, vegetable supplies are considered.

Figure 3.1 illustrates the sources of some vegetables throughout the year.

The home grown season generally runs from May to October. However, some items can be sourced from the UK throughout the year by a combination of alternating regions (Cornwall has an extended growing season), the use of glass houses for growing, alternating varieties through the year (e.g. potatoes), and the use of controlled temperature and humidity storage.

In spite of the above, it is generally cheaper to source and transport products from overseas than to invest in, and maintain, controlled growing conditions throughout the British winter. Spain is a large source of our out of season vegetables; however, Africa is a developing market and offers huge potential for the future.

The flexibility needed to source these products should be reflected in the specification. Ideally, a chart should be issued that indicates, month by month, where the product is likely to have been sourced, whether it has been subjected to any specific storage conditions, whether variety changes will be necessary and when they are likely to occur. There may also be gaps in the chart that indicate that this component, therefore your product, is seasonal and therefore will not be available all the year round.

All of these issues should be raised and discussed with your clients in advance. They can then confirm if a seasonal product would be acceptable and allow for subtle changes because of a variety or supply change when they carry out routine assessments of the finished product.

Wherever the raw material is sourced, it is important that UK and EU law is not breached, particularly in regard to pesticide MRLs. To this end it is better to work to an agreed contract so that your supplier can grow, or contract audited growers to produce, to your needs. The alternative is to buy on the open market, which causes more difficulty in establishing traceability and conformity.

Product	Jan	Feb	March	April	May	June	July	August	Sept	Oct	Nov	Dec
Aubergine	Spain	Spain	Spain	UK	UK	UK	UK	UK	UK	UK	Spain	Spain
Broccoli	Spain	Spain	Spain	Spain	Spain	Spain	UK	UK	UK	UK	Spain	Spain
Cabbage	UK	UK	UK	UK	Spain	UK	UK	UK	UK	UK	UK	UK
Carrot	UK	UK	UK	UK	UK	UK	UK	UK	UK	UK	UK	UK
Celery	Spain	Spain	Spain	Italy	UK	UK	UK	UK	UK	UK	Spain	Spain
Courgette	Spain	Spain	Spain	Spain	Spain	UK	UK	UK	UK	UK	UK	UK
Garlic	Spain	Spain	Spain	Argentina	UK	UK	UK	UK	UK	Spain	Spain	Spain
Ginger	China	China	China	China	China	China	China	China	China	China	China	China
Leeks	UK	UK	UK	UK	Spain	Spain	Spain	UK	UK	UK	UK	UK
Mushrooms	UK	UK	UK	UK	UK	UK	UK	UK	UK	UK	UK	UK
Onions	UK	UK	UK	UK	UK	UK	UK	UK	UK	UK	UK	UK
Peppers	Spain	Spain	Spain	Spain	UK	UK	UK	UK	UK	Spain	Spain	Spain
Potatoes	UK	UK	UK	UK	UK	UK	UK	UK	UK	UK	UK	UK
Spring greens	UK	UK	UK	UK	UK	UK	UK	UK	UK	UK	UK	UK
Spring onions	Mexico	Mexico	Mexico	Mexico	Mexico	Mexico	Mexico	Mexico	Mexico	Mexico	Mexico	Mexico
Tomatoes	Spain	Spain	UK	UK	UK	UK	UK	UK	UK	UK	Spain	Spain

Fig. 3.1. Sources of fresh vegetables throughout the year

3.9 Establishing Risk

It is important to establish the risk of a product in order to ascertain what tolerances are acceptable, whether the product should be positively released and how often, or even whether, it is necessary to audit the factory producing the product.

Risk is measured in degrees. It would be easy to allocate degrees of risk from one to ten; however, for practical purposes, it is usual to stick to high-risk, low-risk, and, where applicable, medium-risk.

- Low-risk materials tend to be robust ambient storage products, e.g. dry goods that will undergo further processing, such as cooking, which will eliminate any residual risk they may have.
- Medium-risk products tend to be high-moisture and -protein products, e.g. dairy and raw meat, where distribution and storage conditions are critical to ensure that potential and spoilage organisms and pathogens are kept at a manageable level that further processing can deal with. Medium-risk also covers products that require a critical process at the supplier's, which may not be apparent in the finished product but is critical to the product integrity, e.g. organic segregation controls.
- High-risk products are where you are completely at the mercy of the controls of your supplier, e.g. ham or cheese, which is added, unprocessed by yourself, directly into a ready meal.

There are three chief aspects that must be considered when establishing the risk of a new ingredient/supplier. They are microbial issues, non-microbial issues and supplier track record. The basic decision trees used for these areas are shown in Figs 3.2, 3.3 and 3.4.

3.9.1 Microbiological risk assessment

The majority of fresh ingredients start off with a potential contamination by pathogens or toxins because they originate from plants, which are generally grown in soil, and/or animals, which carry a micro loading on their hides and in their digestive systems.

As the fresh ingredient is potentially contaminated, could it support microbial growth and toxin production? For chilled meat the answer is yes. If it is raw mince to be cooked into a sauce then it is medium-risk.

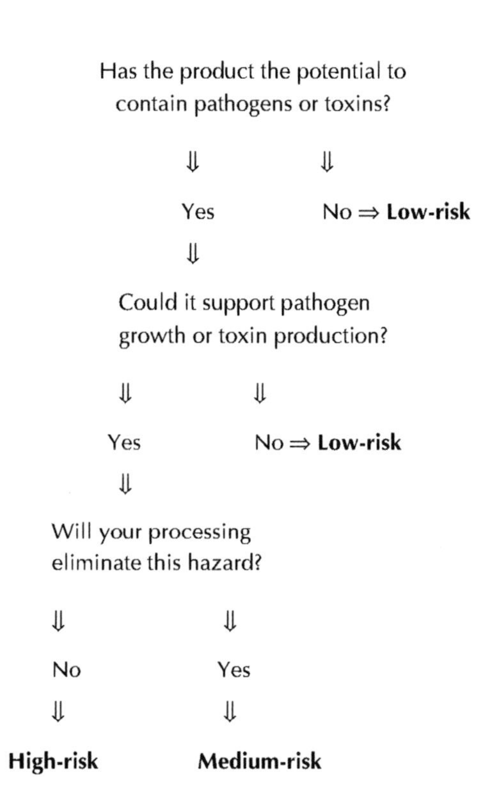

Fig. 3.2. Microbiological decision tree

3.9.2 Non-microbiological risk assessment

The two main areas of non-microbiological risk are chemical (aflatoxins, pesticides, etc.) and physical (stones, glass, vegetable débris, etc.). However, allergens could also be included in this section, e.g. dairy and nuts, or ethical issues such as Halal, Kosher and meat. Control of these issues can be indirect, such as good segregation, traceability and testing systems, or direct, i.e. centrifuging, sieving, sorting or metal detecting.

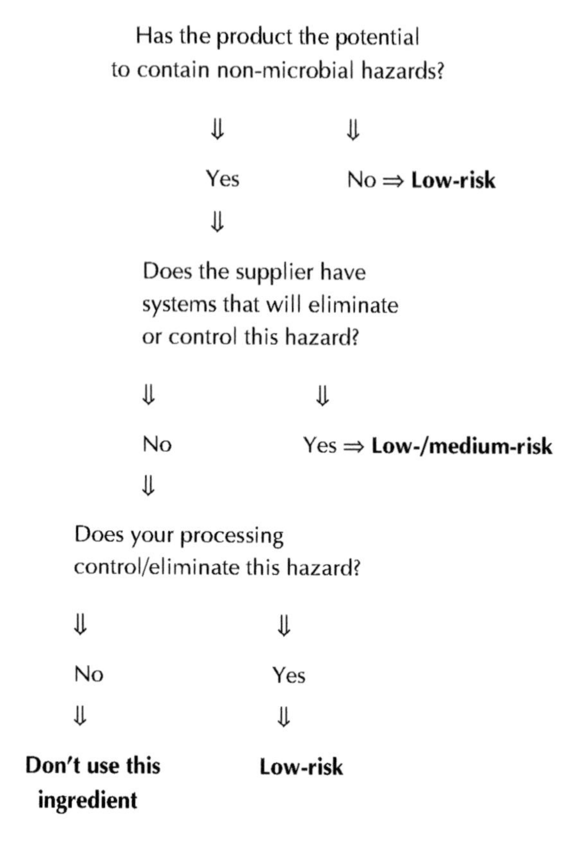

Fig. 3.3. Non-microbiological decision tree

3.9.3 *Supplier risk assessment*

Supplier risk assessment covers how well a supplier is managing microbiological and non-microbiological risk assessment. If issues have been picked up that trace back to a certain supplier, it is important that he is closely managed. If you are dealing with a new supplier, it is also important that he is monitored closely until he has built up a track record of good service.

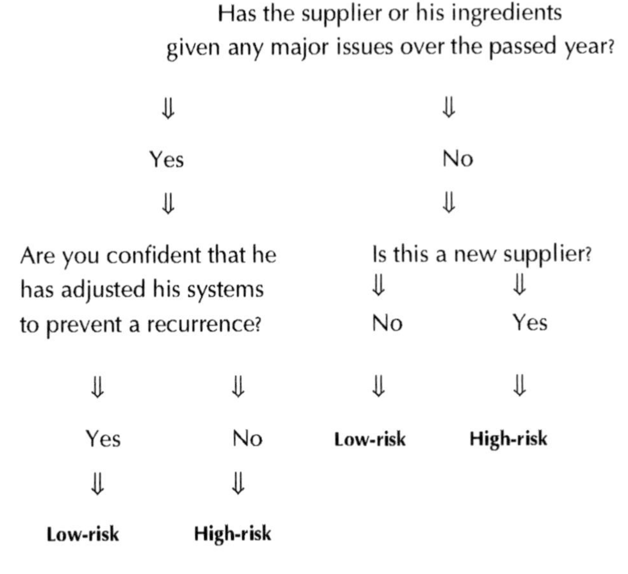

Fig. 3.4. Supplier decision tree

3.9.4 Reaching a conclusion

The decision trees outlined in Figs 3.2, 3.3 and 3.4 give only the thought process that should be followed, not definitive answers. Clearly, the balance of risks and controls at each point for each supplier and ingredient will vary widely throughout the industry. The priorities at each decision will also vary between company, market and product.

If, based on the decision trees, a product/supplier is classified low-risk in two categories and high-risk in one, then always defer to the higher risk. If unsure at any decision point, then err on the side of caution. Even if this results in making an occasional unnecessary audit, it is not time wasted as there is something to be learned from every factory visit.

3.9.5 Frequency of audits

The frequency with which factories should be audited will obviously vary from risk category to risk category. It will also vary within each category depending upon the balance of risk. There are other non-technical issues that can be considered, such as how much of a problem it would be to your business if an ingredient or supplier were to have an issue. Suggested guidelines for audit frequencies are:

Low-risk*:* Suppliers with a low level of risk might not need auditing providing that you have not had any issues with them, and supplier audit questionnaires are sent and satisfactorily returned every 2 to 3 years.

Medium-risk*:* Every 18 to 30 months.

High-risk*:* Every 12 to 18 months.

3.10 Intake Checks

Intake checks cover the basics of product safety and quality and need to be carried out on all incoming materials from packaging to ingredients. Additional critical information can be gathered in the form of either attribute sheets or certificates of analysis specific to the component in question.

Below is listed a set of intake checks that should be carried out on each delivery bearing in mind the variety of the components to be checked, and the limited time and space likely to be available to gather the information in a busy intake area.

The only equipment necessary for the checks below is a keen eye, an inquisitive mind and a thermometer for perishable products.

- **Delivery date/time**: It is important to record dates of deliveries for traceability purposes. Times are particularly useful for monitoring how long perishable ingredients have been standing in an unloading area that might not be temperature controlled. Times are also useful when liaising with suppliers about specific deliveries and following up delayed deliveries.

- **Product name/code**: Confirmation of the product that has been inspected. The code for the product can be yours or the supplier's, preferably one that is used by both. Whichever is used, it must be recognised by yourself and the supplier. With a multi-site operation, it would reduce the risk of confusion if common product codes were established across all plants.

- **Batch number**: This is the traceability code that will be used by the supplier and the factory. It might be the use-by date of the product or a specific code that you apply at intake.

- **Supplier**: You may change suppliers or have more than one supplier for each ingredient; therefore it is important to record the supplier.
- **Date of production**: Not always available, but where it is available on perishable products it should be recorded. This can be used to check that the use-by date corresponds to the correct shelf life.
- **Use-by date**: An opportunity to ensure that the product is within life and will have sufficient remaining shelf life for stock purposes.
- **Inspector**: So that you know whom to contact if there are any queries or discrepancies.
- **Packaging**: Is it clean? Is it intact or punctured? Does it protect the product without contaminating it? Is it in the agreed packaging format (volume, packaging material/colour, etc.)? Were the pallets broken/intact, clean/dirty?
- **Labelling**: Is the labelling clear? Does it state the product, use-by date, storage conditions and any other agreed coding?
- **Hygiene**: Was the transport used to deliver the product clean? Were the containers used to hold the product hygienic?
- **Temperature**: Was it checked where applicable? Record the actual temperature of the product. Does it meet the agreed maximum/ minimum temperature?

3.11 Certificates of Analysis

Certificates of analysis are generally issued as a result of the supplier positively releasing an ingredient for you. They usually cover chemical and/or microbiological information, which allow the ingredient to be used immediately without incurring the cost and inconvenience of positively releasing it yourself. However, from time to time, it is prudent to challenge test the results from a due diligence point of view.

The information on the certificates should have been checked by the supplier before release, to ensure that it meets your specification. However, it is useful for monitoring trends within the specification and for reference if a problem has been traced back to a specific batch of raw material.

When deciding which ingredients require certificates of analysis and what parameters should be covered, it is important that each ingredient is reviewed using a HACCP approach.

Table 3.II shows a range of ingredients for which you should receive certificates of analysis and the parameters that should be covered. You will notice that they tend to be high-protein/-moisture products.

TABLE 3.II
Parameters to be considered on a certificate of analysis

	Milk	Cheese	Butter	Yoghurt	Vegetable oil	Cooked meat
Temperature	*	*	*	*		*
Moisture			*	*		
TVC	*		*			*
Coliforms	*	*		*		*
S. aureus		*		*		*
E. coli		*		*		*
Yeasts		*	*			
Moulds		*	*			
Listeria sp.		*	*	*		*
Salmonella sp.		*	*	*		*
Fat	*		*	*		
Milk solids (non fat)	*					
Peroxide value					*	
Free fatty acids					*	
Protein	*					
Antibiotics	*					
pH	*			*		
Salt			*			

The tolerances permitted for each parameter would largely depend upon any further processing it will receive. Clearly if ham is going to be added to a pre-cooked ready meal, it should, ideally, have a lower micro loading than the threshold permitted for the whole meal. This will allow for a potential increase during handling while portioning the component. However, if a cheese is going to be cooked in a sauce, then the micro loading is less critical, although still important, owing to the potential risk of toxin production, food spoilage, and contamination of your low-risk area and staff with pathogens.

3.12 Raw Materials Attributes

Whilst certificates of analysis can provide the chemical and microbiological information required for the new ingredient, and intake checks give basic information about traceability, packaging and temperatures, they tend to target the safety and legality of the ingredient. However, if the new ingredient is prominent in the finished product, intake attribute sheets can be used to assess the specific *quality* parameters of the material.

Quality parameters of the raw material are critical to the quality parameters of the finished product. If a delivery of diced green pepper has pieces that are too big at intake, they will probably be undercooked in the finished product and the required count will not be achieved in the finished ready meal. Consequently, the specification agreed with the customer may not be met, or the implied agreement with the final consumer, because you do not match the number of peppers that appear on the packaging sleeve.

If the colour, odour or texture is not correct at intake, then, no matter how good your quality systems are down the line, you will produce a substandard product or, at the very least, one that will not perform as it should at the end of its shelf life.

Figure 3.5 gives an example of an attribute sheet.

PART CODE	RAW MATERIAL NAME
M2316	GREEN PEPPER DICED 20mm

INTAKE DATE & TIME :		AMOUNT (Kg) :	
SUPPLIER NAME :		INTERNAL TRACE CODE :	
SUPPLIER D.O.P :		USE BY DATE :	
CHECKER :			

SHELF LIFE :	Production + 2 days, delivered on day of production.	Y	N
PACKAGING :	10 kg tied undamaged blue bags in clean plastic tote bins	Y	N
LABELLING :	Each bag / box labelled ? Product name and size on label ? Use-by-date clearly printed ?	Y Y Y	N N N
DELIVERY TEMPERATURE :	<10 °C Record actual temperature.	Y	N

SIZE :	>80% to be 20mm ± 5mm (Rough squares) Record 10 actual sizes :	3	2	1
COLOUR :	Consistent bright green colour throughout. (Refer to photo)	3	2	1
TEXTURE :	Firm, crunchy	3	2	1
ODOUR :	Fresh characteristic colour.	3	2	1
SPECIAL CHECKS :	Free from softness, rots or moulds and blemishes.	3	2	1
OVERALL QUALITY ATTRIBUTE SCORE :		**3**	**2**	**1**

3 - Meets full specification   2 - Acceptable, but improvement needed   1 - Reject

ACTIONS / COMMENTS :

Fig. 3.5. Example of an attribute sheet

- **Size**: Critical for portion control as discussed above. Exactly how the product is measured and what tolerances are acceptable must be agreed with the supplier in order for it to be workable.

- **Colour**: Pantone references can be used, but it is not recommended for fresh ingredients such as vegetables where, even on the healthiest products, there are likely to be colour variations from top to bottom. It is probably better to have a written description backed up by photos indicating acceptable and unacceptable samples.

- **Texture**: Imagination needs to be used to describe this attribute, because, in most cases you are unlikely to have a statistical standard. Words such as 'firm' , 'crisp' and 'crunchy' are commonly used for vegetables. However, if something should crumble when broken, e.g. a digestive biscuit, then there are no rules to say you can't use that description. It might be unconventional, but if it is accurate everyone knows what you mean and that, at the end of the day, is the objective of the exercise.

- **Odour**: Similar to texture. Describe the smells as accurately as you can in terms that everyone can understand.

- **Special checks**: These are very specific and can cover anything from the absence of secondary skin on onion slices, to the cooking of cauliflower, to checks for greying.

Each aspect is assessed and given a score from one to three. A score of three indicates that all attributes were met in full and that no further action need be taken. An overall score of three can only be given if every attribute listed scores a three.

A score of two is given to aspects of the attribute sheet that were not matched completely but did not warrant a rejection. They will, however, require remedial action from the supplier to ensure that the defect is not repeated. An overall score of two is given even if there is only one attribute that scores two and the rest score three. If a product scores two it is important that a record is made of the supplier contact and the agreed action he will take.

A score of one is given to attributes that are unacceptable. An overall score of one is given even if there is just one attribute with that score, and the batch is rejected. Obviously, the supplier needs to be contacted to uplift and replace but equally important is the fact that the batch is not replaced with similar material. Therefore, details of the attribute(s) that caused the rejection must be given so that appropriate action for the replacement and future deliveries can be taken.

It is useful, where attributes are used, to give a copy to your supplier so that he can check the attributes that are important to you himself before despatch. This can help save you, and him, the inconvenience of rejections.

3.13 Rejections

Although the objective of all of the systems discussed so far has been to eliminate rejections, they will happen. Therefore, it is important that there are systems in place to manage them with the minimum disruption, and draw what can be learned from an unwanted situation.

Figure 3.6 gives an example of a non-conformance form that could be used for raw materials.

RAW MATERIAL NON-CONFORMANCE SHEET

NOTICE OF NON-CONFORMANCE / REJECTION OF RAW MATERIALS SUPPLIED

SUPPLIER :	CONTACT NAME :	POSITION :
TEL :	FAX :	
FROM :	POSITION :	
RAW MATERIAL NAME :	PART CODE :	
AMOUNT (Kg)	SUPPLIER DOP / BATCH CODE :	
TRACE CODE :	USE BY DATE / CODE :	
RAW MATERIAL NON-CONFORMANCE ISSUE :		
ACTION TO BE TAKEN BY SUPPLIER :		
ACTION TAKEN	ACCEPT / REJECT	BY : .... (print name)
SIGNATURES :	TECHNICAL / QA :	DATE :
	STORES :	DATE :
	PRODUCTION/PLANNING	DATE :
	BUYING :	DATE :
SUPPLIERS - PLEASE RETURN RESPONSE DETAILED IN THIS SECTION, OR ATTACH A RESPONSE LETTER WITHIN TWO DAYS (UNLESS STATED OTHERWISE) TO THE QA MANAGER COMMENTS / FOLLOW UP ACTION FROM THE SUPPLIER : (Attach letters)		

Fig. 3.6. Example of raw material non-conformance form

3.13.1 *The decision*

Crunch time! Does the raw material meet the agreed attributes? This decision should be kept as easy as possible by maintaining a clear set of measurements and tolerances that must be checked for each product.

Manufactured ingredients should remain relatively constant throughout the year; however, fresh raw materials are never exactly the same from month to month or even day to day. Therefore, it is important that, for each measurement, there is a workable tolerance agreed with the supplier that is acceptable to you for the process in which this product will be used.

With clear and agreed attributes, it should be simple to take the decision as to whether a product meets the parameters.

3.13.2 *The judgement*

If it has been decided that the product delivered does not meet the agreed attributes, there is a non-conformance. Should it be rejected or accepted? The simple answer would be to reject it and 9 times out of 10 that is the correct decision. However, if the agreed delivery temperature is 1–3 °C, the ingredient will be cooked on site, the certificate of analysis tells you the micro loading is very low, this company has been supplying you product without a problem all year, and the temperature is 4 °C. What would you do? In this case, I believe that nothing would be gained by rejecting it provided that you feel confident that the supplier will address the issue. The key aspect to consider is: 'Will this affect the safety or quality of the finished product?'

In all cases, if there is an issue that requires a product rejection, more than one pallet should be checked, and the driver should be allowed, or even requested to make his own checks before contacting the supplier. This corroboration should limit any later disputes.

It is important that the supplier is made aware of the non-conformance in order that action can be taken to prevent a recurrence. Occasionally, these non-conformance situations may indicate that the tolerances need to be reviewed.

3.13.3 *The communication*

If a rejection is made, it is important that, apart from the supplier, the buying, planning, production and stores functions in-house are informed so that contingency plans can be made to cope without this ingredient, which, clearly, would have a planned use.

When communicating with the supplier it is important that a clear reason for the rejection, quantities, batch codes and product identity codes are given to ensure that he has the tools to uplift and replace the material with good product and, just as importantly, carry out an investigation into how the situation arose.

The supplier should be asked for an initial opinion as to what has gone wrong and a note made, but bear in mind that he is likely to need time to gather information before he can give you a comprehensive answer.

3.13.4 The follow-up

Clearly, any product that is sent to replace the first delivery should be checked particularly closely for the parameter that caused the first delivery to be rejected.

Having asked the supplier for his initial response, it is important that a full and timely written response is received, which lists the factors that caused the non-conformance, the reason why these factors were not picked up and the alterations that have taken place to the quality system to ensure that these factors are picked up next time.

3.14 The Future of Raw Materials

The future of raw materials is dynamic. There are four critical elements that will dictate the future of raw materials; they are information technology, the speed of change, the range of supply, and the 'Organic Effect'.

3.14.1 Information technology

With the advent of 'The Net' and its increased use, it is clear that the speed with which a whole variety of information can be gathered and disseminated will be increased many fold. I also believe that many forms of analysis will be shortened so that a product will spend less of its shelf life uselessly in storage awaiting results for positive release.

3.14.2 Speed of change

The consumer is becoming more widely travelled, intercontinental rather than international, and this is leading to a wider exposure to cuisines and ingredients, which in turn leads to a greater expectation for variety when they return home. The speed with which ready meals are being developed increases year on year as the retailers compete for this consumer who is becoming more discerning. The winners in this market will be the suppliers who can develop and modify products quickly and seamlessly to keep the consumer interested.

3.14.3 *Range of supply*

There are developing markets of raw materials in Africa and, as transport gets quicker and cheaper, there will be a greater reliance on raw materials from Asia and Australia. This will also access a greater variety of raw materials that will allow product development teams to be even more creative. The only thing that I can see reversing this wider range of supply is the 'Organic Effect', whereby transportation might be seen as part of the environmental impact of an ingredient; therefore it is important that transport systems continue to compete and develop along green lines.

3.14.4 *The 'Organic Effect'*

Owing to numerous food scares, the growing mainstream acceptance of organic food and increased awareness of the industrial effect on the environment, food is likely to start to become more 'low-tech' in the use of ingredients, packaging and the processing given. There are also likely to be fewer manufactured compounds used in the production of finished products. This will increase industry's reliance on good-quality, fresh raw materials.

The raw material market is likely to move towards a wide range of fresh ingredients. Their freshness and speed of use will be essential because there will be less reliance upon packaging and additives to enhance shelf life. This will be helped by improvements in transport and communication and a wider supply of raw materials.

The time of being able to carry out a 'virtual' intake check of product before it even leaves the supplier's premises in Kenya for delivery the next day might not be too far away.

3.15 Conclusions

A ready meal is little more than a combination of processed raw materials, however we may try to dress it up. If any of the raw materials are wrong then the product will be wrong.

As we start the new millennium, I believe that the 'processing' part of the ready meal formula will be reduced and consequently raw material quality will become even more important.

It is my hope that this chapter will give you the tools to meet the raw material issues of today and prepare you for the challenges of tomorrow.

4. DESIGNING THE PROCESS

Howard Griffiths

4.1 Introduction

It is important not to forget that the goal for a new factory site or process facility, allowing for the usual commercial constraints, should always be to design the manufacturing process for the requirements of the products to be made in it. The requirements of the product should not be constrained by the process. It is unfortunate that reality often gets in the way of this ideal and, particularly in an existing production facility, the product profile has to be modified to fit the plant layout and process equipment available. For the purpose of this chapter, the ideal situation is discussed and the assumption made that the food technologist has a free hand in designing the process, since it is not possible to second guess the layout, equipment and problems of particular factories. The areas discussed may then be interpreted for situations found in specific production facilities.

4.2 General Considerations

It is assumed in the following discussions that the general fabric and services available for the process facility are adequate for the purpose and that normally recognised rules of Good Manufacturing Practice (GMP) apply (1,2) (see Chapter 6).

The complexity of the products to be manufactured will have a large effect on process design.

A good philosophy to adopt is to design the process to the "worst case", usually most complex, product types likely to be manufactured during the working life of the facility. Product development and process design must always be very tightly linked if successful product and process combinations are to be achieved. This is just as important when new products are being introduced to an existing process as when the new product is subject to a new process situation. Product and process development is usually an iterative process involving a number of feedback loops to gradually match and fine tune product requirements with process capabilities. One of the distinctions of ready meals is that they are multi-component products. Care must be taken during each product/process development stage to allow for the effects on one component of others in the product (see examples later in this chapter).

Chapter 2 discusses "The Development Process" and should enable the food technologist to determine the quality level, storage type and shelf-life requirements of products. These attributes, in particular the last two, will have an impact on selection of the manufacturing process to be used and may even have to be modified in view of the limitations (financial or technical) imposed by available processing options.

It is important (indeed it is usually essential) to ensure that process design is a manufacturing team effort. Every faction within a manufacturing operation has ideas concerning the perfect process: product development staff may like total process flexibility so that any component can be put in any order in any presentational format at any time for any number of products; production staff may like the most simple and quick process, capable of being run with the minimum number of staff and with minimum down time between products, etc. Each area of manufacturing has its own expertise, and process design will be poorer for ignoring any one of them.

The decision on which type of process to use will often depend on which area of food manufacturing the company making the decision is comfortable with, i.e. where its area of experience lies. It is often worth the effort of looking outside this area of experience at the design stage to see what other processing options are available. Caution should be exercised when buying in expertise from outside the company (consultants or equipment manufacturers) to avoid mistaking expertise in selling equipment for knowledge of manufacturing processes.

As discussed in Chapter 1, ready meals can be manufactured in a variety of formats from ambient to frozen to chilled (in order of shelf-life stability), or sometimes combinations of these. It is by these formats that supermarkets and consumers tend to segregate these products, so it is worth discussing a few general points relating to them.

4.2.1 Ambient stable ready meals

Ambient stable ready meals are naturally shelf stable. This may be either by virtue of low water activity (i.e. "just add water and heat" products), or by heat-preserving products in cans, bottles or flexible pouches, having subjected them to a heat process sufficient to give a 12 log reduction in *Clostridium botulinum* and perhaps other "hurdles", plus whatever is required to achieve "commercial sterility" for the prevailing conditions of storage and sale. Ready meal options for both of these formats are somewhat limited. Many raw materials cannot be considered, as they would not survive the drying or heat processing used. In the case of dried ready meals, success depends on the method of water removal, the effects that this has on ingredient, component and product stability or quality, plus the permeability of the packaging to moisture and light. Ambient ready meals in bottles, cans and flexible pouches are constrained by the effects of heavy heat processing on ingredients, components and products. In the case of bottles and cans, but perhaps less so with pouches, there are limitations imposed by packaging shape. Drying and canning technology are both outside the scope of this book, but in general terms the principles discussed here are applicable in the preparation stages of these processes.

The main expansion of ready meal manufacture in the UK and mainland Europe is in the areas of chilled and frozen foods. This chapter is oriented toward these two formats but may be relevant to other areas. Ready meal manufacturing processes will be discussed in this chapter by considering the order in which they most often follow on from one another in terms of process flow.

4.2.2 Frozen ready meals

Frozen ready meals (stored at less than –18 °C) have the advantage of stability but carry an energy penalty for preservation and certain restrictions on presentation and ingredients options (e.g. salads do not freeze well).

4.2.3 Chilled ready meals

Chilled ready meals (stored at 0 to 8 °C) can use a wide range of raw materials; quality retention can be very good, supply chain management (raw materials and finished product) can be a challenge, and both pathogenic and spoilage microorganisms may be a significant risk.

4.3 Standards for Production Areas

4.3.1 Good Manufacturing Practice (GMP) areas

GMP areas are those designed to handle foodstuffs to good basic standards, presenting minimum risk to foodstuffs. These areas are suitable for raw material intake, storage, plus primary and secondary preparation of ingredients and handling of packaged finished product. They are also suitable for manufacture of raw ready-to-cook products.

4.3.2 High-care areas

High-care areas (2) are those designed to minimise product contamination by microorganisms. They are suitable for the manufacture of raw ready-to-eat products and assembly of those products that contain cooked and raw components and are designed to be cooked by the consumer.

4.3.3 High-risk areas

High-risk areas (3) are those designed to prevent product contamination by microorganisms. They are suitable for assembly of fully cooked products that are designed to be eaten cold or reheated by the consumer.

4.4 Product Format

4.4.1 Raw products

Raw products are assembled without any heat processing and need high-quality raw materials and high standards of handling to achieve good product quality. They may need other processes to be applied (e.g. modified-atmosphere packaging (MAP)) to achieve the required shelf life for chilled products.

4.4.1.1 Raw, ready-to-eat products

Raw, ready-to-eat products are designed to be eaten without cooking by the manufacturer or consumer. This makes such products particularly sensitive to contamination by pathogens, since any microorganisms not removed at the raw material or manufacturing stage will be carried through to the final product.

4.4.1.2 Raw, ready-to-cook products

Raw, ready-to-cook products are designed for domestic cooking by the consumer. Most processing operations for raw, ready-to-cook products may be carried out in a GMP area although some may require a high-care area for reduction of spoilage risks. Stir-fry mixes of vegetables and protein would be classed under this group.

4.4.1.3 Raw product considerations

- Raw, ready-to-cook products are designed to be cooked only once (by the consumer) and therefore delicate ingredients such as seafood, some meats or vegetables, whose quality would be greatly damaged by more than one cooking process, are suitable.

- Pathogens that should be rendered harmless by normal domestic cooking processes (non-spore formers and those having heat-labile toxins), are less critical in raw ready-to-cook products than in those designed for domestic re-heating or eating raw. The extra expense of providing a manufacturing environment complying with high-care or high-risk standards (see Chapter 6) may therefore be avoided.

- Spoilage will probably be more of an issue for raw products than for ready meals manufactured from cooked components. For raw products, spoilage is usually the limiting factor for shelf life. Raw materials must therefore be chosen with a great deal of attention to quality level and microbial freshness.

- Storage and domestic cooking instructions for the consumer must be as clear as possible for raw, ready-to-cook products since, on the one hand, undercooking may lead to pathogen survival and on the other, overcooking may lead to unacceptable deterioration in eating quality.

- Leaving the cooking of a product to the consumer does mean that care will have to be taken during product design (Chapter 2). Attempts should be made to ensure that cross-reactions between ingredients, particularly the enzymes, acids, colours and flavours produced during the long shelf life before cooking, or the domestic cooking process itself, do not lead to deterioration in cooked product quality. This may require the introduction of a marinating or some other treatment stage in the process to introduce a barrier to minimise an undesirable effect.

- Filling options for raw products are much the same as for other ready meals. These are discussed in the Assembly section of this chapter.

- Preservation and storage options for raw products are freezing (but not for delicate components) or chilling. Chilled raw products may be packed using a modified atmosphere. This is discussed in the Assembly section. There is a third option of using gamma-ray irradiation. While this is a legal and safe option in most countries, it is not popular, owing to adverse public perceptions concerning ionising radiation.

4.4.2 *Cooked ready-to-eat products*

Cooked ready-to-eat products are designed to be eaten cold or to be reheated by the consumer (possibly to temperatures lower than 72 °C) prior to consumption. Those products that the consumer is expected to reheat before eating need careful control of the cooking process at the manufacturing stage. Cooking in the factory should usually be to the minimum level needed to achieve food quality safety for components of the product. Further heating by the consumer of a product that has already been overcooked by the manufacturer will do nothing for product quality.

4.4.3 *Mixed-format products*

Mixed-format products consist of a mixture of cooked and raw components and may be designed to be eaten raw, reheated or cooked by the consumer – for example, pizzas or salad meals containing cooked proteins or sauces.

The combination of raw meat, seafood or vegetable ingredients with cooked sauces is possible providing that spoilage organisms and moisture or enzyme migration (particularly amylase) from the raw components do not adversely affect the shelf life of the cooked sauce in the combination.

4.4.4 *Special cases*

Products for particular dietary groups such as vegetarians, allergy sufferers and other special groups will require consideration of further segregation in the manufacturing process to avoid cross-contamination with materials that would be a problem for them (4).

4.5 Layout

Some general observations for process layout are:

- Straight process flows with minimum distances and delays between stages are usually the most effective.
- Designing minimum practicable storage of perishable raw material and work in progress (WIP) stocks into the process is often a good idea. Human nature dictates that ways will be found to fill any free space available in a system. Too much available chill space often leads to accumulation of too much WIP, with consequent difficulties in controlling stock rotation and storage life.

- Manual processes are relatively simple, flexible, slow and easy to clean, have high running costs but low capital costs, and usually have lower yields.
- Mechanical processes are relatively complex, inflexible, fast and difficult to clean, have low running costs but high capital cost, and usually have higher yields.
- Poor process design and selection of equipment can result in the worst of both manual and mechanical worlds.

4.6 Equipment

Equipment should always be purchased with its context of use in mind. It must not only perform its required function to a satisfactory standard of quality and reliability but also present the minimum risk to the product and the manufacturing environment in terms of physical or microbial contamination. For example, a dicing or slicing machine may be of little value if, despite its perfect performance in size reduction, it sheds metal or oil into the product or requires a 12-hour strip down and re-assembly for it to be cleaned adequately for use in a high-risk environment.

4.7 Raw Material Storage

Storage of raw materials for ready meal manufacture is no different than for any other area of the food industry and requirements are similar for all factories. Special considerations of raw material selection are covered in Chapter 3. Raw material intake and storage facilities should be appropriate to the materials involved and the use intended for them (1,2). Legal requirements and those necessary to achieve optimum quality and maximum storage life of chilled ingredients may lead to segregated storage, temperature and humidity control of meat, seafood, dairy and vegetable products.

4.8 Ingredients Preparation

The goal here is to determine how much of it you want to do yourself. To obtain the answer, you need to know the quality level and degree of control that you want or need to have.

The option to achieve the least complex process but tending to be the most expensive route, is to buy all the raw materials in a state where they merely require unpacking and placing in final product packaging. This will place a proportionally greater emphasis on the raw material specification and procurement aspects discussed in Chapter 3. Use of "ready-to-pack" raw materials requires that suppliers (and you) must understand the effects of their raw material on your process in great detail since you will have neither the facilities nor the desire to modify a delivery of their non-conforming material to fit to your specification. This can be a particular problem for chilled ready meal manufacture, as chilled ingredients are often delivered "on the day for the day", leaving little or no time to acquire supplies of alternative material if there is a problem with a delivery.

For smaller processing units with simple ingredients, sufficient labour and low production throughputs, preparation of ingredients in house is a viable option. This will need a good level of staff training in the required quality parameters and result in high labour charges, but may also give process flexibility and ingredient freshness in achieving the required quality levels from variable raw materials. Such an approach will enable ready meals manufacturers to be master of their own destiny as far as preparation of raw materials is concerned. In-house preparation may be the only option available to achieve an adequate quality level for highly perishable materials, notably certain fresh vegetables and seafood, particularly if subsequent processing is absent or is only just sufficient to render them stable within the required shelf life. The geographical location of the factory relative to sources of supply will also be a consideration.

4.8.1 Primary preparation

Cleaning of raw materials is important for removal of physical, chemical and microbial contaminants. For vegetables, this may consist of washing in water, with or without the use of surfactants or antimicrobials such as chlorine and its derivatives, ozone or UV. For all materials, cleaning may include inspection by humans or optical sorters, X-ray or metal detection, or the use of sieves or flotation separators. The choice of application will depend on the materials involved and the degree of risk relating to the cleaning problem. For example, the presence of stones in a raw material may present an unacceptable risk to both consumers and processing equipment but a slight variation in the texture of an ingredient may not. Reduction in the level of spoilage organisms may be important for raw products but sometimes this is easier to achieve by control of raw material supply quality rather than by in-house treatment. The risks with cleaning processes are that they may damage the material being cleaned or spread pockets of spoilage organisms or other contaminants around the material, perhaps to the point where spoilage occurs more rapidly on cleaned material. This may be a big issue for raw products.

4.8.2 *Secondary preparation*

4.8.2.1 Size reduction

Manual or mechanical slicing or dicing may be required to give a good presentation of the ingredient and to obtain the correct control of ingredients in component portions of the finished product (see piece size comments in cooking and filling sections). Manual methods are the least capital-intensive, perhaps needing no more than knives and cutting boards, but will incur high labour charges and require a high level of training and monitoring to meet and maintain quality standards. If mechanical methods are an option, then particular consideration should be made to the durability of the equipment and its accessibility for maintenance and cleaning of the cutting surfaces. Historically, size reduction equipment has been one of those areas of the food industry where machine design in some cases has not paid enough attention to ease of use and cleaning. There are now a number of items available that are designed for the modern food industry.

4.8.2.2 Marinating and coating

The use of herbs, spices, powders or oils for marinating or coating the product may be desirable for flavour and appearance of components on consumer cooking and may also be essential for product stability during shelf life or cooking. Surface treatment of meat or seafood by manual or mechanical coating with absorbent materials such as crumb flour, starch or gums may be adequate to reduce liquid production to acceptable levels. If a sauce is part of the product make-up, then this may be formulated to absorb some of the liquid produced.

Marinating of meat or seafood may be necessary to achieve storage and cooking properties required by the consumer. This may be as simple as manual immersion in a container of marinade, through to the more effective but costly use of a mechanical tumbler or to the most efficient incorporation of marinade by vacuum tumbling. If mechanical tumbling is considered, then possible wear and tear effects on meat or seafood must be evaluated. If vacuum tumbling is considered, then design and operation of the vacuum unit for ease of cleaning should be confirmed.

Developing products containing complex components requiring preparation by means of expensive equipment may only be a financially viable "in house" option for the medium to large manufacturer due to the high capital cost.

Specialist preparation and supply of very high value ingredients or product components by third parties may be a possible option for small or large companies who may lack the expertise to prepare these items themselves.

4.9 Cooking

4.9.1 General considerations

Cooking is one of the most critical aspects of the manufacturing process, where critical elements of food safety and quality may be achieved or lost. Leaving aside the environmental considerations discussed later (see Chapter 6), it is worth discussing some of the microbiological issues related to cooking processes at this point. It is important to make the distinction between cooking processes that are primarily performed to achieve an organoleptic quality effect on an ingredient or product (such as char grilling and blanching) and cooking processes that are performed to achieve a reduction in or elimination of pathogenic or spoilage microorganisms. Cooking for organoleptic effects may incidentally (and often does) achieve a satisfactory heat process for kill of microorganisms. The largest potential problem area is in the blanching of vegetables or pasta, where cooking is very fast and takes place at a low temperature (65 to 75 °C) calculated to retard enzymic action and colour degradation. While pathogens may be eliminated by such a short cooking process, spoilage organisms will still be a problem if raw ingredients quality is not high.

Care must be taken to correctly match the heat processing of components to their desired storage life and the shelf life of the product. There are four types of heat process given to components of ready meals, related to the pathogen kill of the process, the component storage life and shelf life required for the product.

The following notes are rough guides that must be proved by process experimentation and validation:

1. Uncooked – heat processed (cooked or reheated) by the consumer or not at all. Shelf life at 0 °C to 8 °C (product dependent) is related to the spoilage organisms present in the components used and the rate of organoleptic deterioration of components. This could be as little as 24 h or as much as 10 days.

2. Pasteurisation – at 72 °C for 30 s or equivalent. This should give a *Listeria monocytogenes* reduction of 6 log and a shelf life of 10 days or less at 5 °C.

3. 90 °C for 10 minutes or equivalent – designed to give a 6 log reduction in psychrotrophic *Clostridium botulinum* spores and a shelf life of more than 10 days at 5 °C.

4. 121 °C for a product dependent time – designed to give a 12 log reduction in proteolytic mesophilic *Clostridium botulinum* and a shelf life at ambient temperature of months or years.

Process conditions must ensure that heating of the ingredient is correctly profiled and controlled throughout the component to give satisfactory quality and give a product that is safe as an end result of the cooking process. Problems can arise with cold spots, which may be intrinsic to the cooking equipment used (e.g. heat gradients across grills or ovens) or which may occur only under particular conditions of use (e.g. when a sauce of a particular viscosity is cooked). There can also be risks associated with headspace, (i.e. the air above the component being cooked) of boiling pans and other pieces of equipment. Partially uncooked or raw ingredients may become lodged above the normal heating level, on sides, safety grilles or lids. These areas may not receive an adequate cooking process. Should such ingredients fall into the main body of the component, either during the latter stages of cooking or during discharge, there is a risk of, at best, spoilage or, at worst, food poisoning.

4.9.2 Layout

All cooking processes essential for a product's food safety (as distinct from those that impart organoleptic effects to an ingredient that will be fully cooked later in the manufacturing process) should have separate infeed and outfeed routes, i.e. they should be loaded from one side and unloaded from the opposite side of the equipment. It is preferable to incorporate this separation into a solid barrier or wall as the open nature of some cooking processes presents a high risk of microbial carry-over from splashing, aerosols and operator actions. This barrier technology is very important for foodstuffs that are exposed both before and after the cooking process – e.g. for foods that are loaded from open trays into an open boiling pan or brat pan and taken by hand out of the pan into trays. This risk is much reduced if the cooking process is carried out in a closed cooking vessel and the resulting material is then transferred via pipeline to the trays. If the cooking process has been designed well, the only remaining risks for the transfer process are those of dirty trays, the environment and the operator on the cooked side (see HACCP, Chapter 5).

Transfer of uncooked materials from raw to cooked areas (GMP to high-care or high-risk) is sometimes not given the attention that it deserves and as a result can cause problems. High levels of spoilage organisms and pathogens can be carried into sensitive manufacturing areas on containers of any material that has not been treated by heating or in some other way to reduce the microbial load. If the transfer of non-cooked items into high-care or high-risk areas cannot be avoided, then procedures similar to the following should apply:

- The material must be double-wrapped, the primary wrapping of the material to be transferred having taken place in a similar area class to that of its destination (e.g. high-care to high-care). The inner "clean" pack of material may then be transferred into the high-care or high-risk area, leaving the outer wrapper behind. This technique might be applied to packaging materials.

- The surface of the container should be cleaned and sanitised at the transfer point and then passed into the high-care or high-risk area. This procedure could be used for canned materials or containers of cooked meats that have been supplied from another factory.

4.9.3 Equipment and methods

Cooking equipment types include: grill/char-grill; fry; steam; roast; bake; boil; sous-vide; scraped surface heat exchange (SSHE); plate heat exchange; extrusion/screw cooking; microwave; ohmic; radio frequency.

Some common combinations of food versus cooking method are:

- Meat, fish and vegetables: grill/char-grill; roast; bake; fry; steam; extrusion/screw; boil; sous-vide.
- Rice, noodles and pasta: steam; boil; sous-vide; fry.
- Sauce: boil; sous-vide; SSHE; ohmic; radio frequency.

Composite methods may combine several of the above.

4.9.3.1 Grill/char-grill

This method of cooking has uses that range from giving a light surface colour or charring effect to a component or a finished product, to providing a fully cooked component. It is characterised by relatively rapid passage of the material to be cooked through a flame or area of intense radiant heat such that the outside of the material is quickly sealed at the start of the cooking process. Application of such a high level of dry heat has the advantage of relatively low levels of moisture evaporation or drip loss during the cooking process and good retention of moisture and texture after the cooking process. The very high temperatures involved require careful control, as there may be little time difference between overcooking and undercooking. This can be a major food safety issue, particularly in continuous grills used for full cooking rather than surface searing. Precision of temperature control, variations of temperature within the grill, and the size, shape and density of grilled ingredients all introduce process variation and may require the use of remote data loggers to validate process parameters. Equipment may be heated directly or indirectly by gas or electricity and operate in a batch or continuous mode. Continuous grills may also incorporate primary and secondary cooling at the discharge end. Continuous grills may take up considerable floor space and provide challenges to environmental controls and to cleaning teams. Cooking by this method is usually not the most energy-efficient, but does provide surface effects not possible with other methods. Combined grill and ovens (usually continuous) are sometimes used to get the best of both cooking options. In fact, if you reduce the temperature and extend the time of most indirect grills, the effect is fairly close to using an oven.

4.9.3.2 Ovens

Ovens may be batch or continuous, and heated directly or indirectly by gas, electricity or steam. Batch ovens can be static or rotary. Most ovens can be used to achieve roasting at high temperature, baking at medium temperature and steam cooking or blanching at lower temperature (if steam is available) by a combination of convection and radiant heat, with the former usually being the most prominent. Controls vary from single manual temperature switches to complex microprocessor management of cycling through wet and dry heat at various temperatures. Comments made relating to grills apply to ovens to some extent, although the more even temperatures of ovens make control and process validation somewhat easier. Remote data loggers may have to be used for process validation in rotary or travelling ovens operating at high temperatures. Process variables for grills apply to ovens.

4.9.3.3 Deep frying

Deep frying is used for a variety of materials, giving them a crisp, well sealed surface and tender interior. Materials that lose moisture easily may suffer unacceptable yield reduction or may not be suitable for frying owing to foaming problems in the frying oil. There will be an increase in oil content due to frying medium retention.

4.9.3.4 Stir frying

Stir frying can achieve good surface colour and production of flavours with minimum loss of texture. It is suitable for small pieces of vegetables, meat, and the more robust of fish species, and for developing flavours in spices. Equipment ranges from the traditional wok for small batches, through brat pans to steam or oil-jacketed horizontal cookers. Validation and monitoring of temperatures achieved can be difficult.

4.9.3.5 Steam cooking

Steam cooking in ovens or steaming pans may be used for a range of ingredients that need cooking without imparting any additional flavours. It is an efficient method for heating as the latent heat of condensing steam is transferred to the surface of the ingredient. Steaming works well for free-draining ingredients but can make smaller ingredients cooked in trays too wet. There may also be problems with ingredients that have a surface coating, as this may be washed off by the condensing steam. Prolonged steaming may lead to flavour leaching in some cases.

4.9.3.6 Boiling

Boiling is used for some solids such as pasta and rice, but it is most widely used for production of sauces and pastes. Equipment used ranges from simple gas or electrically heated, open-topped, manually stirred boiling pans through to steam or oil-jacketed closed pressure vessels having scraped surface stirrers and direct cooling. Cooking of thin sauces with particulate ingredients can cause problems in cooling and filling operations as the solids may tend to separate from the sauce. Problems with ingredients settlement in sauces must be considered at product development as they are not easily rectified later. For example, a difficult situation may be created by combining two particulate ingredients of widely differing densities (e.g. baby carrots and whole fresh button mushrooms) in the same sauce. Unless there is very vigorous agitation in the cooking vessel, which in itself can cause significant damage to ingredients, the mushrooms will tend to float and the carrots will tend to sink. If thinly sliced mushrooms and carrots are used, however, the viscosity of the sauce comes into play more and there is a chance of being able to hold both of them in suspension at once. Problems of ingredients separation in sauce cooking can easily be carried on to the decanting, cooling and filling stages if care is not taken.

There are various mechanical strategies for reducing the separation of components in sauces. These range from changing the profile or axis of the agitator used to introducing a recirculating pump into the system. They all have the disadvantage that they are putting mechanical energy into the sauce and are therefore introducing a potential for damaging the very components that they are trying to suspend and the sauce matrix. There is no substitute for discussing the application with suppliers of equipment and arranging cooking trials before purchase. Separation of components may only be overcome in some cases by removing certain components from the sauce and adding them separately at the assembly stage.

Cooking of sauces with small particulate ingredients and pastes is possible using scraped surface or tubular heat exchangers. Smooth sauces and very thin pastes can be cooked using plate heat exchangers. All of these systems can also be used for cooling operations. They do have the advantage that materials are processed in enclosed equipment and therefore have a minimum risk of environmental contamination. Enclosed systems such as these do have higher levels of process loss and may have a capital cost higher than that of traditional boiling pans.

4.9.3.7 Blanching

Blanching is used as a light thermal process (as little as 60 °C for a few seconds), which heats a material just enough to deactivate enzymes that would otherwise cause colour or flavour loss or lead to textural deterioration of a component (e.g. pasta). The transient nature of the blanching process leads to its main problem area, that of getting the heat into and out of the material fast enough. Techniques used to achieve rapid blanching and cooling include the use of cooking and quenching tanks, steam or microwave blanching followed by water or refrigerant gas quenching.

4.9.3.8 Sous-vide

Sous-vide cooking (5) may be used for finished product processing or, increasingly in the modern chilled food industry, for providing good-quality intermediate components having a long storage life. The strict definition of the term is applicable only to a narrow range of foods. These are cooked at low (often less than 75 °C) precisely controlled temperatures, for long periods of time (often many hours), to give a cooked material of very high quality, which is then rapidly cooled, often using the same piece of equipment in which it was cooked, to a temperature of less than 3 °C. The cooled material is then stored at this same low temperature for many days until it is reheated for serving. Sous-vide was developed for, and is still used in, institutional catering. Its use, in the strict sense of the term for food manufacturing, is difficult since normal retail and catering food distribution chains do not run at less than 3 °C. The very good quality, high yield and long storage/shelf life of the sous-vide process does lend itself to use as a provider of part-processed materials for ready meal manufacture. Meats, fish and vegetables may be cooked and cooled according to sous-vide principles and stored at less than 3 °C for days if not weeks before use without significant loss of quality. Equipment used for sous-vide usually has water or steam as its heating medium and almost always water as its cooling medium since the precise temperature control needed is difficult (but not impossible) to achieve using air heating in an oven.

4.9.3.9 Other methods

Other methods of cooking products exist, including hybrid equipment incorporating aspects of several cooking types and the newer technologies such as ohmic, electromagnetic induction, microwave, and radio-frequency heating.

Cooking is most commonly used for components of products but there are products that are heat processed after filling into their inner packaging as a key critical control point of their manufacture. These may be products that have been assembled from cooked components and are being pasteurised to prolong life. Some products may be assembled raw, then heat processed after packing so that they can be cooked, reheated or even eaten without further heating by the consumer. This strategy is most commonly used for casseroles or other meat- or vegetable-in-sauce products and has the advantage that most of the manufacturing operation may take place in a GMP area. The price paid for this is that packaging has to be more robust and is therefore more expensive. All ingredients are held within the final pack so that there is minimum or no loss of flavour or moisture and product yield is maximised (to 100% if packs are sealed before cooking). Unless care is taken at the product development stage, migration of flavour and colour within the finished product may be a problem.

Sometimes, heat processing is carried out in open packs, which are then lidded and sealed in a high-risk area after cooking (usually baking). Heat processing may consist of baking, roasting, steaming (used for packs sealed after cooking), immersion in heated water, microwave or RF cooking to achieve anything from sous-vide to pasteurisation to commercial sterility.

4.10 Cooling

4.10.1 General considerations

When ingredients, components or products have been cooked, they must be cooled quickly to avoid growth of pathogenic or spoilage organisms that have survived the cooking process or have subsequently contaminated the heated material after cooking. Rapid cooling is also important to maintain quality and avoid overcooking. Usually, but not always, components will be cooled immediately after cooking. Hot filling is discussed in the filling section.

Cooling options vary, but a basic principle is that the optimum cooling rate should be 1 °C per min through the danger zone (65 to 10 °C). This should ensure that the risk of spore outgrowth is minimised.

4.10.2 Layout

Similar rules apply as for the previous sections. Cooling systems are best operated as straight-line processes with entrances to, and exits from, cooling processes sited remotely from one another, with the discharge of cooled material preferably being directly into a refrigerated area. Holding of chilled and hot material in the same space does not make thermodynamic sense and is microbiologically hazardous.

4.10.3 Equipment

Blast chilling takes place in a chamber constructed with cross-flow of air chilled by a large refrigeration plant and deflected across the chamber full of racked foodstuffs by a series of baffles. Blast chillers rely primarily on forced air convection for cooling of the surface of the foodstuff and passive conduction within the foodstuff, and this is not as efficient as the principle used by SSHEs. Careful design of the chiller is essential to obtain the correct velocity and even distribution of flow. Careful consideration of the upstream process and the potential loading of static blast chillers is needed as they are at their most efficient when operated as a batch process. Introduction of hot material to a blast chill chamber half full of cool material will usually cause the cooled material to rise significantly in temperature. It is a better strategy to fill one chamber at a time and ensure that you have enough chambers so that you can use them in rotation without having to mix hot and cold product. Two-stage blast chillers are sometimes used, having a primary stage using ambient air and a secondary stage using chilled air. Design of racks, spacing of trays and placing of material to be cooled on the trays are important factors in optimising the performance of blast chillers. Cooling in unlidded flat trays up to 50 mm deep is fairly efficient. Cooling in 25-kg buckets is extremely inefficient and is microbiologically dangerous. This is mainly a basic physical function of the volume to surface area ratio of the container.

Continuous blast chillers with automatic tracks for racks are used and spiral blast chillers having spiral belts rather than racks are common for larger throughputs. Foodstuffs are sometimes placed directly onto the moving belts in spiral chillers. Cooling in lidded trays to reduce evaporative losses and microbial contamination is possible although less thermally efficient. Cleaning, storage and filling of trays all cost time and money.

Hygienic design is a critical factor for blast chillers, particularly so for spiral chillers. Should the air passing across the foodstuff being cooled become contaminated by dirty racks, trays, or the fabric and cooling elements of the chiller, then the foodstuff will become contaminated. Blast chillers should be designed so that they can be cleaned thoroughly at least on a daily basis and must be designed so that the recirculating air is as clean as possible. Filtration or other decontamination options for the recirculating air flow should be considered.

Cooling tunnels and spiral chillers may use refrigerant gases or liquids such as nitrogen or carbon dioxide, particularly for freezing operations. Fracture damage of the foodstuff being chilled may be a problem if careful control in the direct application of liquid refrigerant is not practised. Removal of waste refrigerant gases may be an operator safety issue.

For sauces and pastes, other options are available in addition to those mentioned above. Many of these options are mechanically similar to those used to cook the material.

4.10.4 Scraped surface cooling

Scraped surface cooling may be used either in the original cooking vessel or in separate vessels, using tubular or scraped surface heat exchangers by means of a jacket circulated with a refrigerant liquid such as ethylene glycol solution. The thermal efficiency of this process (as with blast chilling) is dependent on the volume to surface area ratio of the vessel used, the temperature and flow rate of the coolant and the conductivity of the vessel wall. Cooling is primarily by conduction to a surface that is continually re-exposed by cycling of the scraper and also uses a strong forced convection component from the mixing action. This is more thermally efficient than convection cooling by air. Cooling in the same process vessel as used for cooking, for example in a boiling pan fitted with both steam heating and glycol cooling jackets, will be high in capital equipment cost; cooling may not be as rapid as for other methods and may take up valuable time in the cooking vessel. There is little or no risk of environmental contamination using this all-in-one cook and cool method providing that atmospheric venting is correctly filtered. A separate batch cooling operation will release the cooking vessel more quickly but will increase the capital outlay required. Continuous cooking and chilling is possible by use of in-line scraped surface, tube or plate heat exchangers for cooking and cooling, although plate heat exchangers are only available for use with thin, smooth sauces. Continuous cooking and chilling systems for sauces are fairly complex and usually require the incorporation of CIP (cleaning in place), which is a complex subject outside the scope of this book. They also restrict recipe options to fairly simple "add all ingredients, heat and cool" operations that may not suit complex product requirements.

4.10.5 Mixed-phase cooling

Several times in this section it has been mentioned that bulk containers of sauces do not chill as efficiently as small ones, owing to the physics of surface area to volume ratios. This effect is most pronounced for blast chillers and least for scraped surface chillers. There is a method for achieving fairly rapid chilling of sauces in volumes up to about 8 kg that does not involve the complexity of operation and cleaning of scraped surface, tube or plate heat exchangers and avoids the decanting, washing and contamination risks of blast chilling.

It is possible to hot fill flexible plastic packs with sauce and then immerse these packs in a tank containing circulating, directly or indirectly chilled liquid that will then chill the contents of the packs. This in itself is not much more efficient than blast chilling. If the tank is agitated, however, by being rotated or by use of turbulent flow, then the combined conduction effects inside and outside the packs increase chilling efficiency considerably. If the loading ratio of packs to coolant is sufficiently high, then massaging of the packs takes place, forcing the convection efficiency even higher. There are several manufactures supplying such plant. It is sometimes used for hot-filled sauce based finished products in flexible pouches, but also has applications for preparation of sauces for further processing. Provided that the packaging material is clean prior to filling, the sauce is hot and the sauce delivery system is of hygienic design, quite long storage lives of filled pouches can be obtained.

4.11 Product Assembly

4.11.1 General considerations

The filling operation may seem like one of the easier aspects of ready meals production, but it can create more problems than all the rest put together if care is not taken to design both the product and the process correctly. Having taken great care to get the right raw materials, prepare, cook and cool them in the right way, one might think that it should be an easy matter to put them into a container. Apart from the more obvious dangers of microbiological and physical contamination, especially for products requiring high-care or high-risk preparation, there can be obstacles in the way of putting the correct amount of ingredients in the pack in the correct way.

4.11.2 Layout

For all assembly lines, the ideal of straight lines, short distances and minimum delays holds as true as for other areas, if not more so. The aim, as always, should be to keep foodstuffs exposed to the environment of the filling area for as little time as possible. This is important to minimise heating and microbial contamination of components and product by the assembly line environment. Storage of ingredients for assembly is probably best done immediately prior to the line infeed, although a single dedicated assembly line could have chills at its sides. Separate storage areas may be needed for packaging dried and chilled ingredients. Chilled ingredient storage may well have to be separated for fully cooked and uncooked ingredients to reduce the risk of microbial transfer in high-care areas. Working stocks of components should be kept as low as possible to minimise microbial and quality deterioration. This latter point is often an urgent imperative for hot-filled components.

Simple assembly lines using little mechanical equipment and a high level of labour have less capital cost, and are flexible but are relatively slow. Achievement of product quality and hygiene standards depends mainly on the calibre of staff and the training that they are given. This "human solution" is best suited to short runs of relatively complex products.

Complex mechanical assembly lines using few staff have a high capital cost, and may have a reduced flexibility for the number of possible component additions, packaging sizes or shapes, but can be very fast. Achievement of product quality and hygiene standards depends mainly on the design of the filling equipment and the integration of the equipment into process line.

In designing the assembly process, you must decide how many products you need to fill at any one time, to determine how many lines you need. This may be governed as much by customer delivery requirements and the shelf life of the products as for the number of product lines of short shelf life ready meals. It is often the case that chilled ready meal factories have to make every product every day. For a product portfolio of 50 or 60 this can be quite a challenge and will probably require more than one line.

The complexity of products will have a great effect on line design. An assembly line for a single product having one filling stage and one size or shape of packaging is much more simple (perhaps just a table) than one that has to handle multiple products having many filling stages involving deposits of solid and liquid phases and several pack sizes. It may also be the case that assembly lines have to allow for products that have similar components but are filled in a different order of addition.

It would be preferable to have one assembly line on which products could be filled one by one, the line cleaned and sanitised then the next product filled in series. In practice, this is rarely possible and assembly areas have to accommodate multiple lines for all the reasons stated earlier. Given the reality of multiple lines, a useful strategy in some circumstances may be to have one "spare" line available so that, when a production run is finished, there is usually a new line ready to start the next product. In this way, production staff are always occupied in assembling product and there is usually a spare line that is being cleaned by hygiene staff. Poorly run assembly and cleaning operations happening at the same time in a confined space can be a disaster, resulting in safety risks to staff and contamination risks to product, so careful design and planning are required to make it work effectively.

Products consisting of fully cooked components should be assembled in areas (usually high-risk) physically separated from those used to assemble partially cooked or uncooked meals.

4.11.3 Filling equipment

This should be designed and installed with a view to fulfilling the obligations of the weight legislation relating to the product type, the requirements of the product specification and the consumer expectations of the packaging illustration and publicity for the product.

4.11.3.1 Filling of solids

Manual filling may only require weight scales, scoops or cups. Hand weighing equipment may be of the traditional direct readout (mechanical or electrical) or count down (subtraction) type. Volumetric filling is possible for components that are of a small piece size and have a consistent density. It may be appropriate to fill high-value, consistently sized components or those declared by unit rather than weight, by piece count. Experienced, skilled staff may be able to deposit components into packaging very accurately by eye after suitable training. It is surprising how sensitive and accurate this may be, particularly if accurately weighed target packs are displayed at the filling station for reference.

Mechanical fillers may be vibratory or volumetric or a combination of both. Vibratory fillers were first used for dried and frozen foods but are beginning to find their way into chilled food plants. They are suitable for filling fairly rigid, free-flowing, non-sticky and non-coated materials such as vegetables, cooked diced meat or pasta pieces. Single- and multi-head fillers are available depending on the complexity of the components and filling speed required. Multihead fillers tend to be used for the more difficult materials requiring faster filling speeds.

Volumetric fillers (single- and multi-head) are applicable for materials having a small, uniform particle size, such as rice, small vegetables (peas or diced carrot) and certain types of pasta. There are likely to be compaction and density variation issues that will need to be addressed during feasibility tests with volumetric fillers.

Multi-head vibratory and volumetric fillers tend to be rather complex and can introduce some major but not insurmountable hygiene problems. They often incorporate two- or three-stage cascades (from coarse to fine) to achieve control, and this usually results in a somewhat open architecture for the equipment. This in turn can give the process designers an interesting challenge in minimising temperature and microbial contamination effects from the environment and achieving a high standard of cleaning of equipment.

Mechanical fillers perform best when fed with consistent material at a consistent rate. Several factors conspire to make control less than ideal, including variations in raw material and component texture, size and shape; component cooking, cooling and storage conditions; temperature of filling; and the effects of line stoppages (temperature rise and material compaction). Build-up of product debris in filler surfaces can be a big problem for the accuracy of fill and for ease of cleaning.

4.11.3.2 Filling of liquids

Manual filling by volume requires only jugs or cups for equipment, although this can be achieved by weight rather than by volume if preferred.

Mechanical volumetric fillers come in a variety of formats from single-head piston to multi-head rotary devices depending on the properties of the liquid, the speed demands of the process and the budget available. Equipment cleaning is a big consideration for high-care and high-risk operations. Options range from strip-down and manual cleaning of small simple fillers to sophisticated CIP for complex fillers.

4.11.3.3 Cold or hot fill?

When filling sauces and possibly (but more unusually) solid components, it is worth comparing the options for cold and hot filling. Hot filling is generally considered to be filling above 72 °C (i.e. above a vegetative pathogen kill temperature). Cold filling is for components at 8 °C or less.

Cold filling is by far the most common method found in the chilled food industry. The issues for cold filling are:

- WIP storage times for cold-filled components are measured in hours, days or even weeks. This compares favourably with the storage times for hot-filled components, which are often a matter of minutes.
- The relatively long component storage times mean that the assembly stage of manufacture does not have to be a carefully scheduled just-in-time operation. See the hot filling issues (below) for those problems.
- The equipment for handling cold materials is generally less expensive than that used for hot filling since it does not have to be tolerant of rapid changes or prolonged exposure to high temperatures.

Hot filling of components is commonplace in the canning industry and, if executed correctly, may have advantages for chilled foods. The issues for hot filling are:

- There is less opportunity for microbiological problems with correctly designed hot filling, since levels of some potential spoilage organisms and pathogens (in the component and on contact surfaces of equipment and packaging) may be reduced by virtue of pasteurisation or similar heating effects imparted by the hot component.
- Hot-filled components have a very short WIP storage life before use since the cooking process effectively continues (although perhaps at a slower rate) up to the point of filling and subsequent cooling. Careful planning is required at the product development stage to ensure that components are robust enough to withstand the prolonged heat and still deliver the required quality level.
- Careful planning is required when designing the process flow. Process design should attempt to ensure that there are no significant delays in the filling process that may cause deterioration of the hot component beyond its specified limits. Conversely, there should be no significant delays in the cooking process that will cause the filling line to stand idle waiting for product to be cooked. The whole manufacturing operation from raw material preparation, through cooking to filling has to work in synchrony for hot filling to be efficient. This is surprisingly difficult to achieve in any but the most simple of process flows and may be found to be almost impossible for any product having more than two components. It can be all too easy to turn a just-In-time system of manufacture into one that is "just-too-late" by failure of one link in the chain of manufacture.
- Transfer of hot components from cooking to filling areas in trays will incur the greatest heat and evaporative losses. Evaporative losses can cause significant problems of weight and texture loss for hot fill solid components.
- There are potential health and safety problems associated with handling hot materials in trays.
- Transfer from cooking to filling by means of sealed and heated or insulated pipelines or mobile containers will result in less heat loss and almost no evaporative loss.
- Either very high holding temperatures or heated filling equipment may have to be used to ensure that components do not fall below critical temperatures (less than 72 °C) during the filling process. This can be difficult to achieve for batch filling processes and may result in significant quantities of component being rejected for low temperature at the start of production runs.
- Filling components warm (less than 72 °C) rather than hot will result in significantly increased risk of spoilage (possibly even from outgrowth of

spores within the component) and pathogen survival. If hot filling cannot be guaranteed all the time, then cold filling must be used. Any significant delay in the assembly process will probably result in rapid cooling to temperatures that could cause microbiological problems.

- Hot filling of components requires some form of fast chilling (normally after sealing) to reduce the finished product to the correct temperature for storage and distribution.

4.11.3.4 Portion control, piece count control and presentation

One area of ready meal manufacture that is a frequent cause of difficulty is that of getting the right amount of components into the product. Weight control is not the issue here, as it can be achieved with relatively little effort by means of manual or mechanical weighing devices. This section refers to the correct proportion and number of solid components in the finished product that are required to comply with both the legislation relating to the ingredients list and the expectations of the consumer. In short, how many components and how many pieces of each component do you need in the product and what tolerance levels do you have? Success depends on having the correct product formulation at the product development stage and a good understanding of the statistical capabilities of the whole manufacturing process, not just the filling equipment. In physical terms, success depends on the average and range of sizes of the raw material at the preparation stage, the combination and proportion of those materials in component mixtures, (sauces or solids blends), the tendency of the manufacturing process to separate those mixtures and the piece count per material in the correct weight of the component at the filling stage.

If a raw material has a large range of piece weights, it will tend to have a large range of piece counts. If the raw material is a major part of a component or product, this will probably cause problems. A consumer may buy two units of the same product both having the same component weights but one having double the piece count of a major component or sub-component of the other. The one with the lower piece count will probably be perceived as having less of that component. Further problems may arise if the product is a ready meal for two people and there is an odd number of component pieces in the pack.

Even if variation in raw material piece size is not an issue, distribution of particles in a sauce or in a mixture of solids may cause problems if the mixture tends to separate. We have already seen that separation of components in a sauce may be caused by density differences. This is also the case (although less obvious) for solid blends. This may be exacerbated by characteristics of processing equipment, e.g. larger particles being held back in narrow pipes and filling heads or accelerated separation induced by vibratory feeders. Unequal proportions or pieces of different components in a blend may lead to certain of them not appearing at all in the filled product. The dynamics of the filling process and its effect on the statistical variation of piece counts in the finished product need careful consideration and evaluation before deciding on a final product format. In some cases, the only solution to the problem may be to have more filling stages in the assembly process or to fill critical components by piece count rather than weight.

Presentation or arrangement of the finished product in its packaging may or may not be critical. The appearance of products that are presented for sale in transparent packaging will be far more obvious than for those sold totally enclosed in opaque packaging. While the easiest (but perhaps slowest) route to achieving a first class presentation of components in a product may be by use of manual filling, there are mechanical options available for component placement and orientation within the pack. These range from filling nozzles and component templates that direct components to certain positions in the pack to semi-automated pick and place equipment.

4.12 Post-assembly Processing

Modified-atmosphere packing (MAP) is commonly used for shelf life extension of raw and cured meats, fish, prepared vegetables and salads (6). MAP may possibly be employed for ready meals comprising any one of these food types. The MAP regimes used for each of these food types do, however, use quite dissimilar gas mixtures. Use of MAP with mixed-format ready meals comprising, for example, raw fish and prepared vegetables, will require extensive trials to evaluate the potential benefits, as existing knowledge of MAP does not cover the conflicting demands of the various components. MAP may be used for shelf life extension of ready meals consisting of fully cooked components since the main benefits relate to reduction of oxidation and retardation of microbial spoilage. When considering use of MAP for shelf life extension one must be aware of the risk of anaerobic growth (including *Clostridium botulinum*) for food safety. Do not use MAP unless you are sure that you have performed a thorough risk assessment first. Sealing machines that incorporate MAP are available from a number of manufacturers.

Post-assembly heat processing is performed on several types of products that are assembled in the raw state (see section 4.9). For these products plus hot-filled products and cold-filled products that spend a long time in the assembly area, raising their temperature above that required for safe storage and distribution, some form of chilling will be required (see section 4.10). This must be performed quickly to lower the product temperature to the desired range for food safety and, in the case of products that are heated prior to sealing, to minimise yield and aroma loss.

4.13 Packaging

The choice of which food contact packaging to use may be made for purely aesthetic reasons or may be governed by the constraints of the product, or the preservation or storage method used for it. Bottles, tubs, pouches, foil card or plastic trays have all been used for ready meals. Trays tend to be used where product presentation is important. Sealing of trays may be by crimping, pressure, adhesive, heating (from heating elements in the sealing machine or inductive heating of metal foil), or a combination. Easy-peel seals are common for plastic trays and lids used in chilled ready meals.

Bottles, tubs and pouches are most often used for stews and other solids-in-sauce products. Sealing of bottles and tubs may be by means of screw or push-fit tops or using similar seals to those used for trays. Pouches are usually heat sealed.

The normal method of packaging supply for small to medium-sized operations is as the ready to use container and lid. High-volume production units may consider fabricating the packaging from stock materials. While this incurs the additional expense of packaging production machinery, the saving in storage space (for bottles or tubs) or packaging production cost may make it viable. Production volume and speed considerations will probably determine the use of manual or mechanical feeding of packaging to assembly lines.

4.14 Conclusions

The variety and scope of ready meal manufacture are so wide that this chapter can only attempt to provide an outline of some of the options available for ready meal products, process and equipment combinations. It should give the prospective process designer an indication of major pitfalls and plus points in the various areas outlined so that these may be discussed in depth within the manufacturing company, with industry experts and with equipment suppliers.

Key prerequisites for successfully designing the process are being as sure as possible of what products you want to make, how you want to put those products together, what raw materials you want to use and how you want to prepare and process them. Only when you have consensus in these areas can you begin to design the process. Obtaining that consensus may take most of the time in the design stage, since it may involve everyone, from consumers and customers to all members of the company manufacturing team, plus external experts. This should be time well spent, as designing a perfectly good process for the wrong product will probably be just as bad as designing a bad process for the right product. Getting a process design wrong will be an expensive and frustrating experience. Getting it right may still be expensive (in terms of capital cost) but will not only represent good value for money but will also be an enjoyable experience.

References

1. Blanchfield J.R. *Food and Drink – Good Manufacturing Practice – A Guide to its Responsible Management.* London, Institute of Food Science and Technology (UK). 1998.

2. Chilled Food Association. *Guidelines for Good Hygienic Practice in the Manufacture of Chilled Foods.* London, Chilled Food Association. 1997.

3. Chilled Food Association. *Class A (High Risk) Area Best Practice Guidelines.* London, Chilled Food Association. 1995.

4. Lessof M. *Food Allergy Issues for the Food Industry.* Leatherhead, Leatherhead Food Research Association. 1997.

5. Betts G.D. Technical Manual No. 39 – *The Microbiological Safety of Sous-Vide Processing.* Chipping Campden, Campden and Chorleywood Food Research Association. 1992.

6. Betts G.D. Guideline No. 11 – *Code of Practice for the Manufacture of Vacuum and Modified Atmosphere Packaged Chilled Foods with Particular Regard to the Risks of Botulism.* Chipping Campden, Campden and Chorleywood Food Research Association. 1996.

5. HACCP

Bizhan Pourkamailian

5.1 Introduction

Product safety is a concept that must be considered at the design stage of a new product. It is at this point that the question must be asked whether it is possible to manufacture the product safely. The current best known and effective method for the management and control of food safety issues with food production is the Hazard Analysis Critical Control Point (HACCP) system. See Appendix I for glossary of terms with reference to HACCP.

HACCP is a logical science-based system that can help control food safety. It is used to identify and control safety hazards at all stages throughout the food chain, from raw materials through to consumer handling and use. Hazards are identified, analysed and then controlled at critical control points. All food safety hazards are considered – chemical, physical and biological. Monitoring procedures are used to check that control limits are being achieved, while a process of verification is used to ensure that the HACCP system is working effectively.

The main advantage of HACCP is that it can prevent or reduce the chance of food safety hazards arising. More effective control is achieved by focusing technical resources on the key step in the production process.

The EU Hygiene Directive (93/43/EC) requires all food business to identify the hazards in their products, to manage and control them. The obvious way for food producers to achieve this is by use of the internationally accepted HACCP system.

The HACCP approach can be used for the production of almost all products. The use of HACCP in the food sector is now widely accepted and implemented. With the progress of technology and "emerging" hazards, there rises a need for the hazards to be constantly reviewed and updated, as has been the case for *Escherichia coli* O157.

As with any product, HACCP should be considered from the beginning, at the product development stage. A HACCP plan may be drawn up for a product or a generic plan for a group of products, with supplementary additions for specific products. The procedure for developing a HACCP plan is illustrated below.

5.2 Developing a HACCP Plan

The HACCP system is a logical, scientific approach to controlling safety problems in food production. When a company adopts HACCP, it puts controls in place at each point in the production system where safety problems could occur from biological (microbiological), chemical, or physical hazards. To start a HACCP system, a company must write a HACCP plan. This chapter explains how to write a HACCP plan in 14 preparatory steps. These steps can be referred to as the logic sequence in a HACCP plan.

The logic sequence is:

Step 1 Assemble HACCP team
Step 2 Define terms of reference
Step 3 Describe product
Step 4 Describe intended use of product
Step 5 Develop process flow diagram
Step 6 On-site verification of flow diagram
Step 7 Conduct hazard analysis and establish preventive measures
Step 8 Identify critical control points
Step 9 Establish critical limits
Step 10 Establish monitoring procedures
Step 11 Establish corrective action
Step 12 Establish verification procedures
Step 13 Documentation
Step 14 Review HACCP plan

Hummus is used as a product example throughout the chapter. (This case study is an example to illustrate the HACCP approach, and is provided without any liability whatsoever in its application and use).

5.2.1 Step 1 – Assemble HACCP team

In preparing for a HACCP plan, as in any project, a group of people is required that will bring the maximum amount of knowledge required to set up the system. The group of people involved in setting up a HACCP system is the HACCP team. The first and most important aspect of the team will be its need to be multidisciplinary. The team may possibly require the direct involvement of top management. In a small company, the HACCP team may comprise only two people. In order to increase the resources of the team, it may be required to bring in outside expertise. This expertise can be found through a trade or professional association, or a contractor of one's choice.

The expansion of the resources within the HACCP team will allow for the better identification of biological, microbiological, chemical and physical hazards. In a larger company, it may be suitable to bring in employees from different departments, such as production, quality control and engineering, as well as company microbiologists, chemists and product developers. It is always key to include in the HACCP team employees who are directly involved in the daily processing activities. In order to write a HACCP plan, there are some key issues that need to be clear to all HACCP team members. These are:

- The technology used in the processing line
- The equipment used in the processing line
- The basic aspects of food operations
- The flow of process in the plant under examination
- A knowledge of HACCP systems

Although all team members would have a basic understanding of HACCP, it would be very beneficial if the team leader had a clear understanding of how HACCP is applied and why (see Fig. 5.1).

Company:	Safe Foods Inc.	
Team:	HACCP	
Responsibility:	To develop HACCP plan	
Product:	Hummus	
Date:	21 December 1999	
	Name	Position
Team leader:	M. A. Inman	QA Manager
Team members:	N. O. All	NPD Manager
	M. A. Keall	Production Manager
	S. Coty	Engineering
	I. C. Ontrol	QC Manager
	M. A. Doc	Laboratory Manager

Fig. 5.1. Assemble the HACCP team

5.2.2 Step 2 – Define terms of reference

In any management team, it is important to define the terms of reference before commencement. The team must also decide on the scope of the study, i.e. where the study starts and where it stops. An example of HACCP terms of reference is shown in Fig. 5.2.

> This HACCP study will consider all hazards associated throughout the entire production of hummus. The hazards may include biological, chemical and/or physical hazards.
>
> Biological hazards may include parasites such as *Cryptosporidium,* pathogens such as *Staphylococcus aureus* and *Salmonella.*
>
> Chemical hazards may include pesticides, allergens and chemical contaminants from processing.
>
> Physical hazards may include stones and metal from contamination during processing.
>
> The HACCP study will cover the above-mentioned hazards from the point of ingredients received to the point of product despatch.

Fig. 5.2. Terms of reference

5.2.3 Step 3 – Describe product

Complete product description is the third step. The information should include complete data on product composition, physical/chemical structure (including water activity, pH, etc.), microcidal/static treatments (e.g. heat treatment, freezing, brining, smoking, etc.), packaging, durability and storage conditions, and method of distribution. Labelling instructions should also be included as part of the product description. A brief description of how the process occurs and/or the product(s) are produced/prepared is useful, as this will help identify possible hazards that may exist within the ingredients and/or in the packaging materials. It will be necessary at this stage to make a complete list of ingredients and raw materials (see Fig. 5.3).

5.2.4 Step 4 – Describe intended use of product

The intended use should be based on the expected uses of the product by the end user or consumer. In specific cases, vulnerable groups of the population, e.g. in institutional feeding, may have to be considered. Is the product ready to eat or will it be cooked by the consumer? A ready-to-eat product implies that the product must be free from pathogens as it leaves the factory, and so the process must contain sufficient critical control points

(CCPs) to ensure that this is the case. An example of product intended use for hummus is shown in Fig. 5.4.

Product name:	Hummus.
Product type:	Ready-to-eat meal.
Ingredients:	Chickpeas, garlic, salt, lemon juice, vegetable oil and water.
Process:	Blanching, mixing, cooking, cooling.
Preservation:	Combination of pH (4.8), salt (5%), cooking (> 75 °C for > 10 min), and storage temperature (< 7 °C).
Packaging:	250-ml polypropylene tubs.
Distribution:	Product distributed nationwide by land under chilled conditions.
Shelf-life:	Five days at chill.
Label instruction:	All ingredients, possible allergens, shelf life and storage conditions.

Hummus is a ready-to-eat meal made from the combination of cooked chickpeas with garlic, salt, vegetable oil and lemon juice. The final paste is hot filled into polypropylene tubs. The tubs are closed and cooled to chill temperature. The product is chill distributed and given a 5-day in-store shelf life.

Fig. 5.3. Product description

Normal use:	Retail trade.
Intended consumer:	The general public.
Condition to be held:	Refrigerated.
Consumption:	Must be consumed in one sitting.

Fig. 5.4. Product intended use

5.2.5 Step 5 – Develop process flow diagram

A flow diagram should be an accurate representation of the line as it runs, not how it was designed to run. The HACCP team should construct the flow diagram (see Fig. 5.5). The process flow diagram should identify all the steps used to prepare the product from receiving through final shipment that are directly under the control of the establishment. When applying HACCP to a given operation, consideration must be given to steps preceding and following the specific operation. It must be noted that this step is designed to find any place in the specific operation where hazard may occur.

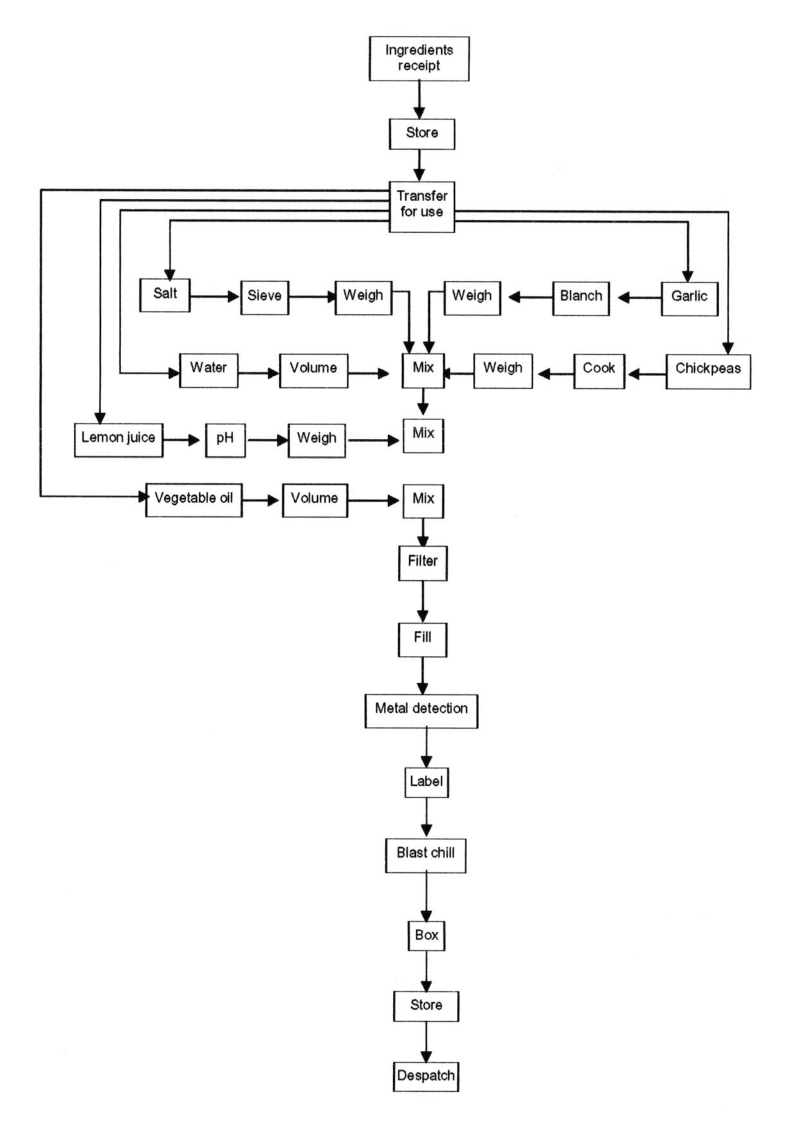

Fig. 5.5. Process flow diagram for hummus

5.2.6 Step 6 – On-site verification of flow diagram

The HACCP team should confirm the processing operation against the process flow diagram by "walking the process line". This should be conducted in such a way that would encompass all practices during all stages and hours of operations. At the same time, information should be collated on the line layout, personnel movement, line and environmental hygiene, connections between pasteurised and unpasteurised products, etc. In light of the information gathered, the flow diagram should be amended where appropriate (see Fig. 5.6).

Has the flow diagram been inspected by HACCP team? Yes/No

HACCP Team Inspector	Date	Shift	Time	Signature
S. Coty	21/12/99	Day	10.30	-----------
I. C. Ontrol	21/12/99	Day	10.30	-----------
M. A. Inman	22/12/99	Night	19.45	-----------
M. A. Keall	22/12/99	Night	19.45	-----------

Fig. 5.6. Flow diagram verification

5.2.7 Step 7 – Conduct hazard analysis and establish preventive measures (Principle 1 – see Appendix II)

At this step, the HACCP team must look at each process step in turn and identify all realistic hazards and any preventive measures that are controlling the hazards. No judgement of the critical nature of the hazard should be made at this stage. The food safety hazards defined by the regulation are biological, chemical or physical properties that may cause a food to be unsafe for human consumption.

In order to be able to identify the biological, chemical and physical hazards associated with food products, knowledge of the microbiology, chemistry and physical properties of the product, as well as the various processes that may affect those characteristics is prerequisite. An understanding of the interaction between ingredients is also essential.

Each step in the process flow has to be evaluated and the introduction of a hazard at each step determined and whether appropriate preventive measures are in place. Hazards that are low risk and not likely to occur should be listed on the hazard analysis and the reason that no further consideration is needed should be stated. These determinations should be based on incidence evaluation and/or scientific data.

Biological hazards are living organisms, including microorganisms, that can put human health at risk. Biological hazards include bacteria, parasites, protozoa, viruses, etc.

Chemical hazards may be naturally occurring poisons, chemicals, or deleterious substances that are natural constituents of foods and are not the result of environmental, agricultural, industrial or other contamination. Examples include aflatoxins, mycotoxins, and shellfish toxins. Chemical hazards may also be added poisons or deleterious substances that are added to the food, whether intentionally or unintentionally. These may be pesticides, fungicides, antibiotics, lubricants, paints or even food additives.

Physical hazards are any physical material not normally found in a food, which may cause illness or injury to the individual using the product. This type of hazard includes glass, metal or plastic. However, foreign bodies that cannot or do not cause illness or injury are not considered hazards in these contexts, even though they may not be aesthetically pleasing to the customer.

Having identified the hazards associated with each process step, it is necessary to conduct hazard analysis of each step. This step involves the identification of the biological, chemical and physical properties in raw materials and processing steps, and an assessment of their likely occurrence and potential to cause food to be unsafe for consumption. Thus this step involves identifying the hazards that are of such a nature that their elimination or reduction to acceptable levels is essential to the production of safe food.

Conducting a hazard analysis should involve:

- Ensuring that the prerequisite programmes are in place.
- Observation of the actual practices in the operation.
- Evaluation of the likelihood of hazard occurrence and severity of their adverse health effects.
- A qualitative and/or quantitative evaluation of the presence of hazards.
- Observation of the survival or multiplication of microorganisms of concern.
- Knowledge of the production or persistence in foods of toxins, chemicals or physical agents.
- Awareness of conditions leading to the above.

Once the hazards have been identified and analysed for likely occurrence and potential to cause food to be unsuitable for consumption, preventive measures must be established.

Preventive measures are defined as the control of an identified food safety hazard by physical, chemical or other means. It may be that more than one control measure is required to control a specific hazard (or hazards) and that more than one hazard can be controlled by a specified control measure. Table 5.I gives an example of a hazard analysis chart for hummus.

TABLE 5.I
Hazard analysis chart for hummus

Process step/ Ingredients	Hazard	Source	Control measure
Ingredients in	Microbiological, physical and/or chemical contamination	All hazards from raw material and/or packaging	Supplier specification – GMP
		Contamination of chemical hazards from migration of exhaust fumes through packaging	Vehicle engines to be switched off on docking – GMP
Dry store	Microbiological, physical or chemical contamination	Contamination of microbiological, physical and chemical hazards from environment during storage	Ensure maintenance of ingredients packaging integrity. Keep all ingredients covered – GMP
		Contamination of chemical hazards from migration of exhaust fumes through packaging	Use battery-operated vehicles within plant – GMP
Transfer for use	Microbiological, physical or chemical contamination	Contamination of microbiological, physical and chemical hazards from environment during transfer	Keep all ingredients covered – GMP
		Contamination of chemical hazards from migration of exhaust fumes through packaging	Use battery-operated vehicles within plant – GMP
Cook	Survival of vegetative pathogenic microorganisms through inadequate heating	Pathogens from raw material and/or contamination during processing	Appropriate cooking process

Continued/..

TABLE 5.1 (contd)

Process step/ Ingredients	Hazard	Source	Control measure
Weigh/ volume	Growth of pathogens as a result of inadequate dosing of key ingredients used to inhibit growth	Pathogens from raw material, contamination during processing and/or pathogens not targeted for destruction during previous steps (e.g. spore formers)	Appropriate weighing of critical ingredients during addition
Blanch	No hazards identified	–	–
In-line sieve/ filter	Foreign material carried through	Foreign bodies from raw material and/or contamination during processing	Appropriate sieve/filter size to reduce level of foreign bodies to acceptable levels and maintenance of sieve/filter
Mix	Microbiological, physical or chemical contamination	Contamination of microbiological, physical and chemical hazards from environment and machinery during mixing	Ensure maintenance of machinery. Keep all mixing vessel lids covered and ensure no possibility of material falling into vessel. Ensure no cleaning residues in vessel – GMP
pH	No hazards identified	–	–
Fill	Presence of vegetative pathogens	Product container	Ensure hot filling to the appropriate temperature
Metal detect	Metal pieces in product not identified	Metal from processing equipment and/or contamination during processing	Appropriate effective metal detector used and set up

Continued/..

TABLE 5.I (contd)

Process step/ Ingredients	Hazard	Source	Control measure
Label	Incorrect labelling of shelf life and storage conditions for ingredients, leading to inappropriate storage and therefore toxin production by pathogenic organisms and/or consumption by at-risk individuals	Spore formers not destroyed at earlier stages of process and not inhibited by product formulation that would exist in raw material	Ensure correct labelling
Blast chill	Growth of pathogens due to inadequate cooling	Pathogenic spore formers that would exist in final product	Ensure appropriate rate of cooling to correct final temperature
Box	Growth of pathogens due to increased product temperature	Pathogenic spore formers that would exist in final product	Ensure product packed in such a time not to allow for a rise in product temperature – GMP
Chill storage	Growth of pathogens due to increased product temperature	Pathogenic spore formers that would exist in final product	Ensure storage of product at correct temperature
Despatch	Microbiological, physical or chemical contamination	Contamination of microbiological, physical and chemical hazards from environment during transfer	Keep all ingredients covered – GMP
		Contamination of chemical hazards from migration of exhaust fumes through packaging	Use battery-operated vehicles within plant – GMP

Continued/..

TABLE 5.I (contd)

Process step/ Ingredients	**Hazard**	**Source**	**Control measure**
Despatch (contd)	Growth of spore-forming pathogens due to extended storage period in inappropriately temperature controlled despatch area	Pathogenic spore formers that would exist in final product	Ensure appropriate chill temperature is maintained by transfer from chill storage directly to chilled transport vehicle

5.2.8 Step 8 – Identify critical control points (Principle 2 – see Appendix II)

The decision tree (see Appendix III) is applied to each hazard at each process step to identify critical control points (see Table 5.II). The application of a decision tree should be flexible, given that the operation is for production, slaughter, processing, storage, distribution or other process. The diagram representing the decision tree (Appendix III) may not be the only method for determining critical control points. Other methods may also exist, and the use of the most appropriate method is recommended.

If a hazard has been identified at a step where control is necessary for safety, and no control measure exists at that step, or any other, then the product or step should be modified at that step, or at any earlier or later stage, to include a control measure.

5.2.9 Step 9 – Establish critical limits (Principle 3 – see Appendix II)

For each critical hazard, limits and target values are set for the preventive measure. The limit divides acceptability from unacceptability; the target should be set based on the operational variability of the process to ensure that it remains within the limits. Critical limits must be specified and validated, if possible, for each critical control point. In some cases, more than one critical limit will be elaborated at a particular step. The criteria often used include measurements of temperature, time, moisture level, pH, a_w, and sensory parameters such as visual appearance and texture (see Table 5.III for details of critical limits).

TABLE 5.II
Critical control points identified

Process step	Q1	Q2	Q3	Q4	CCP	CCP No.
Ingredients in	Y	N	N	–	No	–
Dry store	Y	N	Y	Y	No	–
Transfer for use	Y	N	N	–	No	–
Cook	Y	Y	–	–	Yes	1
Weigh/volume	Y	Y	–	–	Yes	2
Blanch	N	N	–	–	No	–
In-line sieve/filter	Y	Y	–	–	Yes	3
Mix	Y	N	Y	Y	No	–
pH	N	N	–	–	No	–
Fill	Y	Y	–	–	Yes	4
Metal detect	Y	Y	–	–	Yes	5
Label	Y	Y	–	–	Yes	6
Blast chill	Y	Y	–	–	Yes	7
Box	Y	N	Y	Y	No	–
Chill storage	Y	Y	–	–	Yes	8
Despatch	Y	Y	–	–	Yes	9

See Appendix III for details of questions (Q1–Q4) and critical control points (CCPs)

5.2.10 Step 10 – Establish monitoring procedures (Principle 4 – see Appendix II)

Monitoring is essential to a HACCP system. Monitoring is a planned sequence of observations or measurements to assess whether a CCP is under control and to produce an accurate record for future use in verification. The monitoring procedure must be able to detect loss of control of the process to prevent violating the critical limits (see Table 5.III). Where possible, process adjustments should be made when monitoring results indicate a trend towards loss of control at a CCP.

5.2.11 Step 11 – Establish corrective action (Principle 5 – see Appendix II)

HACCP is a preventive system, and, to correct problems before they affect the safety of the food, advance planning to correct potential deviations from established critical limits is required. If at any time a critical limit is not met, there needs to be a corrective action in place. Corrective action should be set to tell the operator what to do if the CCPs move outside their limits. The action must ensure that CCPs have been brought under control (see Table 5.III). Action taken must also include proper disposition of the affected product. Not all deviations can be anticipated; therefore, it is recommended that the statement "other actions as appropriate" be included with the specific corrective action.

5.2.12 *Step 12 – Establish verification procedures (Principle 6 – see Appendix II)*

This is a very important part of a HACCP system. Once the HACCP system has been implemented, it should be verified continually to ensure that it is working as it was intended to (see Table 5.III). This can be carried out through auditing methods, procedures and tests, including random sampling and analysis.

Examples of verification procedures are:

- Ensuring that CCPs and critical limits are adequately controlled and monitored.
- Ensuring that employees are following established procedures for handling product deviations and record keeping.
- Identification of verification frequencies and location of results records.
- Recording details of verification procedure and documenting for future reference.
- Review of modifications of the HACCP plan.
- Sampling and testing to verify CCPs.

Examples of when verification should be conducted:

- Routinely and occasionally unannounced.
- When new emerging concerns regarding food safety occur.
- In order to confirm that changes to the HACCP plan have been implemented properly.
- To assess whether it is necessary to modify HACCP plan as a result of changes in product.

Verification reports may include information on:

- The records that are associated with CCP monitoring.
- Calibration records and certificates.
- Records for corrective actions.
- Training and knowledge base of workers responsible for monitoring CCPs.
- Validation activities.

TABLE 5.III
Table of critical control points (CCPs)

Process step	Hazard	Preventive measure	CCP No.	Critical limit	Monitoring	Corrective action	Verification
Cook	Survival of vegetative pathogenic microorganisms through inadequate heating	Appropriate cooking process – target 75 °C for 10 min	1	Minimum product internal temperature of 70 °C for 2 min	Cooking temperature and time continuously recorded on chart recorder and visually inspected for every batch	Place product on hold in appropriate place. Report to Quality Assurance Manager to discuss options of rework or discard	Product temperature of first batch measured every day
Weigh/ volume	Growth of pathogens as a result of inadequate dosing of key ingredients used to inhibit growth	Appropriate weighing of critical ingredients during addition	2	Minimum 5% w/w salt, 50% w/w water	Addition is measured and recorded on every batch	Place product on hold in appropriate place. Report to Quality Assurance Manager to discuss options of rework or discard	Analytical analysis of final product of three batches once every month
In-line sieve/ filter	Foreign material carried through	Appropriate sieve/filter size to reduce level of foreign bodies to acceptable levels and maintenance of sieve/ filter	3	No foreign material larger than 2 mm in diameter	Sieve checked after each batch to ensure no holes larger than critical diameter	Place product on hold in appropriate place. Report to Quality Assurance Manager to discuss options of rework or discard	Customer complaint data and monthly analysis of product

Continued/..

TABLE 5.III (contd)

Process step	Hazard	Preventive measure	CCP No.	Critical limit	Monitoring	Corrective action	Verification
Fill	Microbiological physical or chemical contamination	Ensure hot filling to a target temperature of 70 °C	4	Product filling at a minimum of 68 °C	Product filling temperature continuously measured in-line and recorded	Place product on hold in appropriate place. Report to Quality Assurance Manager to discuss options of rework or discard	Measure product temperature in tub after filling every hour
Metal detect	Metal pieces in product not identified	Appropriate effective metal detector used and set up	5	1.5 mm ferrous, 2.0 mm non-ferrous, 2.5 mm stainless steel	Every tub passed through metal detector	Run through metal detector; on confirmation, contact Quality Assurance Manager to discuss procedures for metal identification and further action	Metal detector checked with test pieces every 30 min, including at start-up
Label	Incorrect labelling of shelf life and storage conditions for ingredients leading to inappropriate storage and therefore to toxin production by pathogenic organisms and/or consumption by at-risk individuals	Ensure correct labelling	6	Correct label applied	100% visual inspection	Quarantine product until appropriate label can be applied	Ten tubs chosen randomly from storage once every month for thorough inspection

Continued/..

TABLE 5.III (contd)

Process step	Hazard	Preventive measure	CCP No.	Critical limit	Monitoring	Corrective action	Verification
Blast chiller	Growth of pathogens due to inadequate cooling	Ensure appropriate rate of cooling to correct final temperature	7	Product to reach internal temperature of 10 °C in 2 h	Blast chiller temperature continuously measured in-line and recorded	Place product on hold in appropriate place. Report to Quality Assurance Manager to discuss options of rework or discard	Temperatures of 10 tubs chosen randomly are checked after 2 h in blast chiller, once a day
Chill storage	Growth of pathogens due to increased product temperature	Ensure storage of product at correct temperature	8	Minimum product temperature of 4 °C	Chiller temperature continuously measured in-line and recorded	Place product on hold in appropriate place. Report to Quality Assurance Manager to discuss options for action	Temperatures of 10 tubs chosen randomly are checked after 2 h in chiller, once a day
Despatch	Growth of spore-forming pathogens due to extended storage period in inappropriately temperature-controlled despatch area	Transfer directly from chill storage to chilled transport vehicle	9	Product not kept outside chill storage or chilled transport vehicle	100% Visual inspection by despatch operators	Measure temperature of product on top pallet. Report to Quality Assurance Manager to discuss options for action	Temperature of 3 tubs chosen randomly from the top of a pallet are measured, once a day

5.2.13 Step 13 – Documentation (Principle 7 – see Appendix II)

As with all management systems, full documentation and document control are required. It is necessary to keep full and accurate records to establish an efficient application of the HACCP system. Documentation and record keeping must be appropriate to the nature and size of the operation. In accordance with the HACCP principles, the HACCP system should include documentation and records for:

- CCPs
- CCP monitoring activities
- Establishment of critical limits
- Handling of deviations and corrective actions
- Results of verification activities
- HACCP plan
- Hazard analysis
- Modification of HACCP systems

5.2.14 Step 14 – Review HACCP plan

The HACCP plan should be reviewed to determine whether the CCPs and critical limits that have been established are in fact correct and that they are controlled and monitored adequately. It is important that HACCP plans are reviewed at least once a year as well as when changes to the process are to be implemented. Changes may involve, among others:

- Identification of potential new hazards in process
- Change of suppliers or product formulation
- Changes to the process steps or procedures
- Changes to the processing equipment

Appendix I: Glossary of HACCP Terms

The following definitions include proposed amendments to those given in the existing Codex Guidelines for the Application of Hazard Analysis Critical Control Point System

Control (verb)	To take all necessary actions to ensure and maintain compliance with established criteria
Control (noun)	The state wherein correct procedures are being followed and criteria are being met
Control measure	An action or activity that can be used to prevent or eliminate a food safety hazard or reduce it to an acceptable level
Corrective action	A type of action to be taken when the results of monitoring the CCP indicate a loss of control
Critical Control Point (CCP)	A step at which control is essential to prevent or eliminate a food safety hazard or reduce it to an acceptable level
Critical limit	A value that separates acceptability from unacceptability
HACCP system	A scientific and systematic way of enhancing the safety of foods from primary production to final consumption through the identification, evaluation and control of hazards that are significant for food chain under consideration
HACCP plan	A document prepared in accordance with the principles of HACCP to ensure control of hazards, which are significant for food safety in the segment of the food chain under consideration
Hazard	A biological, chemical or physical agent with the potential to cause an adverse health effect when present at an unacceptable level

Hazard analysis	The process of collecting and interpreting information on hazards and conditions leading to their presence to decide which are significant for food safety and therefore should be addressed in the HACCP plan The information considered should include: – the likely occurrence of hazards and severity of their adverse health effects – the qualitative and/or quantitative evaluation of the presence of hazards – survival or multiplication of microorganisms of concern – production or persistence in food of toxins, chemicals or physical agents – conditions leading to the above
Monitor	The act of conducting a planned sequence of observations or measurements of control parameters to assess whether a CCP is under control
Step	A point, procedure, operation or stage in the food chain, including raw materials, from primary production to final consumption
Validation	Obtaining evidence that the elements of the HACCP plan are effective
Verification	The use of methods, procedures, or tests in addition to those used in monitoring to determine compliance with the HACCP plan

Appendix II: CODEX HACCP Principles

Principle 1 Identify the potential hazard(s) associated with food production at all stages, from growth, processing, manufacture and distribution, until the point of consumption. Assess the likelihood of occurrence of the hazard(s) and identify the preventative measures for their control.

Principle 2 Determine the points/procedures/operational steps that can be controlled to eliminate the hazard(s) or minimise its (their) likelihood of occurrence – (Critical Control Point (CCP)). A "step" means any stage in food production and/or manufacture including raw materials, their receipt and/or production, harvesting, transport, formulation, processing, storage, etc.

Principle 3 Establish critical limit(s), which must be met to ensure that the CCP, is under control.

Principle 4 Establish a system to monitor control of the CCP by scheduled testing or observations.

Principle 5 Establish the corrective action to be taken when monitoring indicates that a particular CCP is not under control.

Principle 6 Establish procedures for verification that include supplementary tests and procedures to confirm that the HACCP system is working effectively.

Principle 7 Establish documentation concerning all procedures and records appropriate to these principles and their application.

Appendix III: Critical Control Point Decision Tree

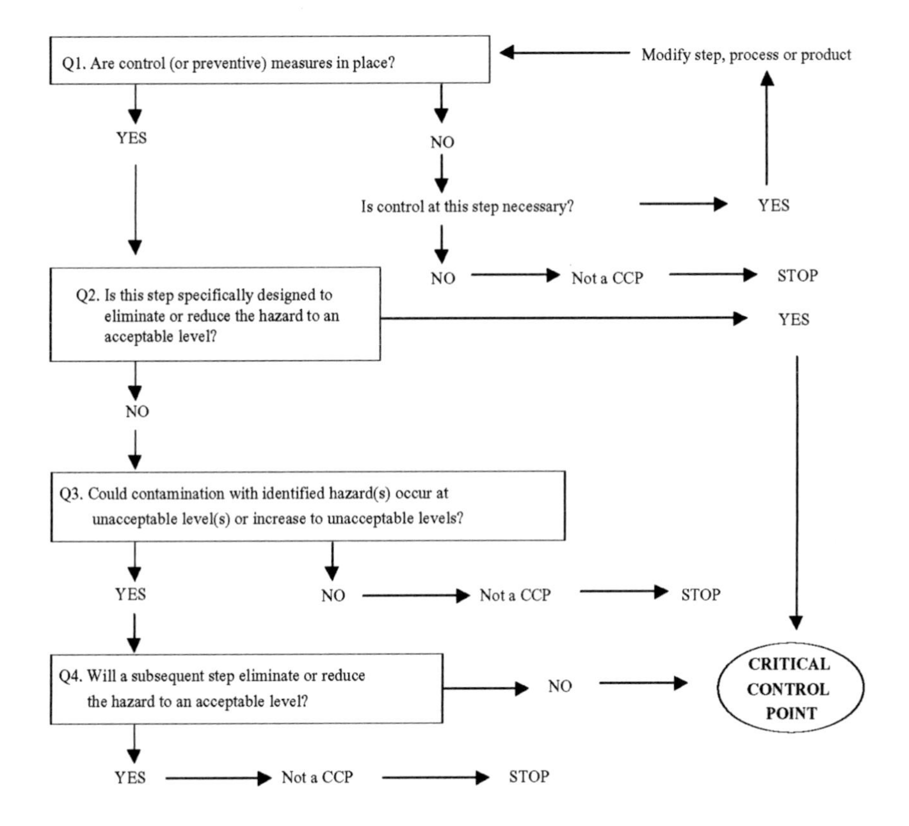

6. MAINTAINING A CLEAN WORKING ENVIRONMENT

David Jeffries

6.1 Introduction

In microbiology, there are no absolutes (1,2) – sampling techniques (3), testing methodology and microbial distribution only allow us to say that the probability of the presence of spoilage and/or pathogenic microorganisms is significant or not, at that specific time. Therefore, clean can mean that there is no visible débris on food contact surfaces and that levels of bacteria are below detectable levels. Consequently, maintaining a clean environment is about implementing and utilising a series of defences that reduce, prevent or eliminate the risk of microbial contamination. There is no end point – only a continuing search for ways to improve cleanliness within the environment (4).

This chapter attempts to highlight the major microbiological risk factors associated with different manufacturing environments, and indicates some of the strategies that may be adapted to reduce the risks. Other physical and chemical factors are covered only where they may overlap with microbiological risks.

Ready meals manufacture is a relatively new technology, which is still developing in terms of our understanding of risk factors and the ways in which we can prevent or control those risks. Some of the factors can interact in quite subtle ways. This makes it an exciting and challenging area for the food technologist; there is still much to learn and apply.

The intention is to highlight the type of risk that may occur and give some guidance on reducing or eliminating those risks. It must be remembered that each operation will have its own balance of factors, which will be dynamic with changes of product, process, people and fabric. The criteria covered are those gleaned from personal experience as well as some theory from research projects carried out over the last few years.

There has been an encouraging increase in research in the area of understanding how to maintain a clean environment and which factors have a significant influence. Basically, risk assessment remains the best way to control and prevent microbiological contamination. It is always easier to build controls into a new process or facility than to have to add them to an existing process or facility where practices and attitudes may have become engrained.

The factors should be considered individually and collectively for each defined area, process and product range. Many factors interact within the arena of activity and can produce quite subtle effects; for example, a cleaning chemical dispensing system installation may give high total viable counts (TVC) owing to a design fault, which in turn manifests itself on the surface of cleaned equipment.

If any of these factors changes, then the risk assessment has to be re-evaluated. All evaluations must be recorded and any actions or improvements clearly documented with clear management responsibilities and timescales. Always check that these items are followed up to ensure that implementation and continuous practice remains in place. Always agree a review date with the relevant management members to avoid 9-day wonders.

Risk assessment should also include a cost analysis – what will it cost if this is not done? This could include loss of sales, personal damage costs, waste, etc. Most of this work involves assessment techniques that would be familiar to insurance companies, which recognise that the cost risk is a key measurement and should be used as part of the decision process. All expenditure within a business has to be justified and cost risk analysis forms part of the technical risk assessment.

Most of the points raised in this chapter are "common sense" and in some cases may seem rather obvious; however, they can easily be overlooked in the bigger picture of project timescale, day to day activity, cost constraints and existing processes. Distractions can be manifold and the challenge for the technologist and hygiene manager is to remain focused on the objectives that they have set.

Temporary fixes should be avoided wherever possible, as "temporary" has a habit of becoming permanent. If a temporary fix is applied, it should be made clear that it is temporary, with dates to remove the temporary fix and replace with a permanent solution, and a suitably qualified person should authorise the implementation of the corrective action.

Simple things done well can be a huge benefit in maintaining a clean environment. In fact, the aim should be to simplify processes and procedures if possible; for example, the process should be as in line as possible, and equipment modified to simplify its disassembly to facilitate cleaning. Finding the most efficient manufacturing flow of material and people will inevitably reduce the microbiological and foreign body risks as well as provide operational benefits. A joint technical and operational "win" is always the preferable option.

The technologist will have specialised knowledge and experience in relation to maintaining a clean working environment, but it is within the context of the factory team that the role will be at its most influential. Selling the principles and rules to the team to ensure their full commitment at all times is of utmost importance.

6.2 Definitions

6.2.1 *High risk*

High risk/high care defines an area within a factory where cooked (chilled ready meals) or prepared food, for example sandwiches and prepared salads, is assembled into a packaging format and that food may receive no further or insufficient heat treatment to pasteurise that product (5). Consumer reheat instructions on the packaging are designed to ensure that the product is reheated to pasteurisation temperatures, but there is no guarantee that the consumer will follow those instructions. It is reasonable for the consumer to expect that the product is free from pathogens and has minimal risk of microbiological deterioration over its shelf life.

To ensure the safety of the final product, people and all items that enter the clearly delineated area must move via clearly defined routes that minimise the microbiological risks and prevent cross contamination.

Physical barriers must be in place to prevent accidental entry to the high-risk area, reduce contamination from work in progress and provide an unequivocal message to all staff and visitors that this area is different from other parts of the factory.

For precooked items, e.g. canned goods, a method for sanitising the surface of the can on entry to the high-risk area is required.

Evacuation of the high-risk area must be covered by a procedure for staff to return to the area in such a way as to minimise the risk of introducing microorganisms into the environment, the sanitising of footwear at the point of entry back into the high-risk area being an example. For food containers, e.g. aluminium foils or cPET trays, a sanitising process may not be feasible, so these items should be delivered from the manufacturer in two polythene bags, the outer of which is removed at the point of transfer into the high-risk area.

Packaging, consumable items, etc., must be assessed for microbiological risk and the appropriate method identified for the transfer into high-risk areas.

6.2.2 *Medium risk*

Medium risk constitutes an area within the factory where uncooked and/or part-cooked components are assembled into a packaging format, e.g. diced or sliced vegetables, prepared cuts of raw meat or fish with a cooked sauce. The consumer reheat instructions are designed not only to pasteurise the product but also to cook it. The area will be physically separate from the low-risk area, with colour-coded protective clothing dedicated to the area. The main objectives are to reduce foreign body contamination risks and to prevent microbial growth. The area will be temperature-controlled but will not necessarily have air filtered to remove airborne microbial contamination.

Transfer of packaging may not necessarily be controlled in the same fashion as in the high-risk procedure.

6.2.3 Low risk

Low-risk parts of the food handling operation cover all areas where materials are handled prior to undergoing a cooking or bactericidal treatment and their subsequent transfer into the high-risk area. Material movement and storage should be arranged to minimise the chances for microbial growth. Foreign body control and the maintenance of the quality of raw materials are also prime objectives. The traceability of materials starts on the farm and continues right through to the plate.

All other areas of the factory must be defined as to the risk factors, and procedures are defined accordingly, but there are no designated areas with different cleaning routines. Other practices of segregation, for example meat from vegetables, or organic material from non-organic, must be in place. A typical chilled ready meal factory layout is shown in Fig. 6.1.

6.3 The Environment

6.3.1 Air quality

6.3.1.1 Contamination risks

Whilst air movement is essential for safety reasons – typically the air is changed 15 to 20 times per hour – other kinds of air movement can cause significant microbiological, and to a lesser extent chemical and particulate contamination.

Filtration of the air for a high-risk area requires filter level 9, which removes 95% of particles down to 0.5 micron, which is sufficient to remove most microorganisms (6). Without the installation of an appropriate filtration system, risks from airborne microbial contamination such as mould spores can cause significant spoilage of finished product.

Whilst air quality plays a key part in reducing airborne contamination, other activities within this environment can also have major impact, as will be described later.

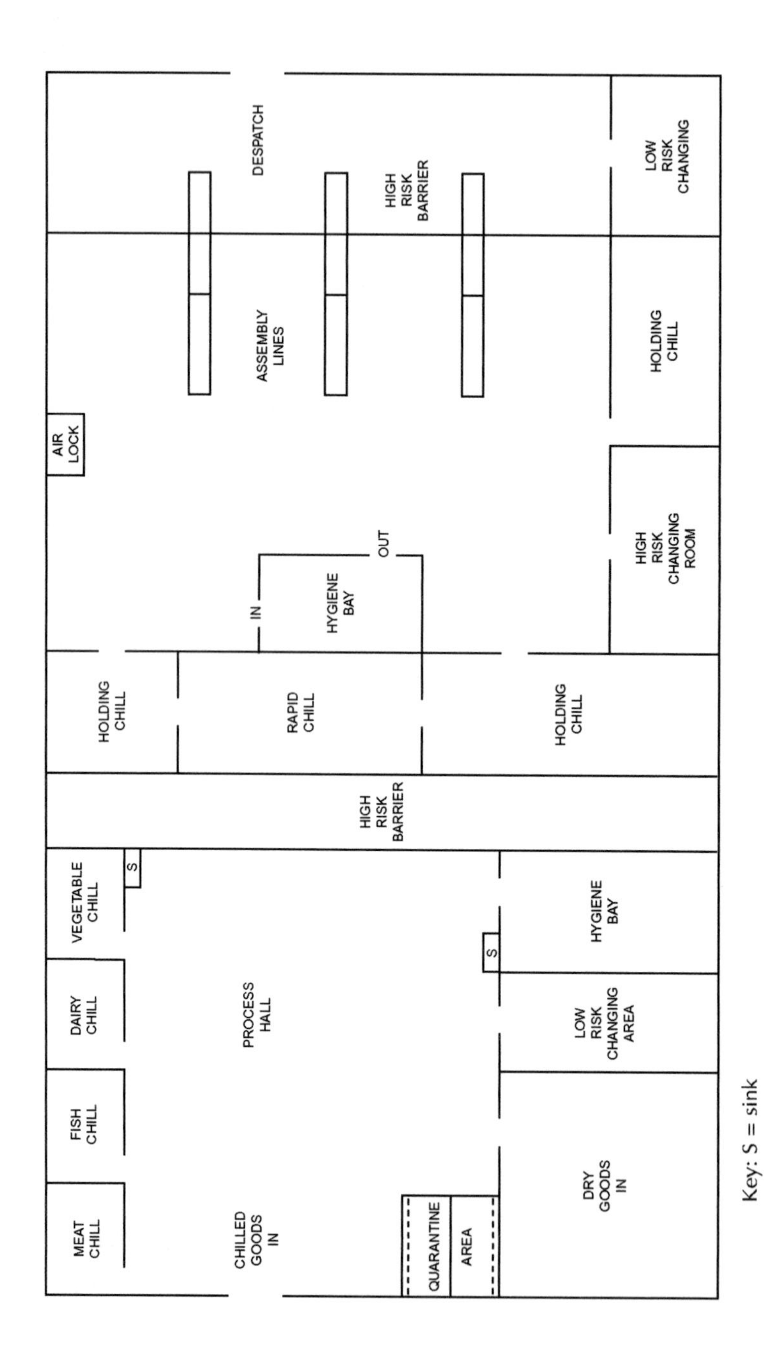

Fig. 6.1. Typical chilled ready meal factory layout

The amount of water has a significant impact on microbiological risk – the amount of water in the environment should be minimised or preferably eliminated during the time when product is being manufactured. Water droplet formation during cleaning activity can spread microorganisms around – a problem that may be exacerbated by excessive or reduced air flow causing condensation.

6.3.1.2 Gross air movement

All high-risk areas must have a positive air pressure in relation to the low-risk areas. There will be a number of air extraction systems within the high-risk environment, including cleaning bays (removal of moisture and traywash steam extraction), steam extraction over cooking vessels, and cooling systems (nitrogen tunnels), in addition to normal air replacement. Transfer systems such as UV tunnels and spraying systems may also have air extraction systems that can upset the air balance. Regular monitoring of the air movements with regard to changes of process is essential and needs to be supported by clear documentation. These factors and any others that may affect the overall air balance must be taken into consideration to ensure that positive pressure is maintained. The regular opening of doors, temperature differentials and air deflection caused by equipment movement (bins, racks, etc.) can all impact on air movement and therefore the risk of microbial contamination.

The movement of air in holding chills and blast chillers should also be considered as providing a transfer mechanism for water droplets from the condenser unit as well as from the floor of the chill if this is allowed to get wet.

Movement of machinery into or out of the high-risk environment can cause unusual air movements and should be monitored closely and linked to specific cleaning and sanitising after the work has been completed. This should be done at periods of minimum activity. Air locks can introduce unfiltered air into the high-risk environment depending on their design. Air curtains are not acceptable with current designs. Electric motors normally have cooling fins attached to the driveshaft and can act as reservoirs for dust and microorganisms. Regular inspection and (dry) cleaning are recommended.

Under no circumstances should air lines be used to clean equipment as this method will spread food particles and microorganisms around the environment.

The use of vacuum cleaners causes high air movement both from the vacuum created and from the air blown out of the motor. Some vacuum cleaners have microbiological filters fitted to the exhaust air, but there is still a turbulent air current created.

6.3.1.3 Temperature differential

Air movement can also be affected by differences in temperature within the environment chills at 0 to 5 °C, working environments of 12–16 °C and localised heating caused by cleaning in place (CIP) systems.

Extraction systems associated with grillers or other high-temperature equipment that may be sited within the high-risk environment can be a major influence on the maintenance of a positive air pressure. This kind of equipment should be given due attention for cleaning effectiveness. Whilst there may be high temperatures within the body of the equipment, cooler areas can still harbour food débris and consequently microorganisms.

6.3.1.4 Humidity

Whilst all effort should be made to reduce the use of water in the environment during production activity, cleaning may use water and thereby increase the humidity within the environment. This can reach 80% relative humidity. Reduction of the humidity from the air and the fabric before the commencement of production is important. The use of a dehumidifying system following completion of cleaning would be useful. Very hot food placed in a chiller can also generate condensation. Ceilings and overhead pipework can be the source of condensation build-up following cleaning activity. This should be removed before production activity starts followed by an investigation to identify the root source of the problem, which should then be eliminated.

6.3.1.5 Measurement of air quality

Sampling equipment for measuring air movement is readily available. Microbiological air quality needs to be assessed accurately. The usefulness of exposure plates is limited as they rely largely on settlement rather than the active removal of airborne particles. The purchase or hire of an appropriate sampler is recommended.

Measurement points need to be identified using the criteria given above.

One sampling device currently available (supplied by F.W. Parrett Limited of London) uses nutrient agar or selective media. There are limitations using air samplers – if they are hand-held, the user can affect the results; therefore, remote activation of the sampler is a useful feature of this product.

6.3.1.6 People movement

The movement of people at shift change and break time can cause significant changes to airflow with the opening and closing of doors. Hand washing creates skin particles, and this should be borne in mind when deciding the siting of hand-washing stations (see section 6.3.4.2). The management of people movement by staggering break times and shift change-over can also help alleviate the situation. Air movement can be used to reduce the microbiological risks by providing a localised airflow over and away from the product assembly line. This has been assessed by CCFRA and the Silsoe Research Institute (8) and is in use in some chilled ready meal factories.

6.3.1.7 Chiller units

Regular cleaning of condenser units throughout the factory is essential and should be linked to a fogging regime and/or the application of a residual biocide. The application of the principles used in the Fogging Handbook (9) is essential. Chiller design should also be considered, as most units have enamelled mild steel casings that can break down with regular cleaning and in turn provide harbourage for microorganisms as well as a foreign body risk. The wire covers on the front of the condenser units can be plastic-covered mild steel; these should be replaced with stainless steel to eliminate a potential foreign body hazard.

The nature of the material stored in the chill and the frequency with which material is used can affect the build-up of organic material within the unit.

An alternative strategy would be to use an ozone generator to reduce the presence of microorganisms within the chiller during use. There are legal limits for exposure to ozone, which must be followed.

Every system will be slightly different and therefore needs an individual risk assessment based on air movement and the measurement of airborne microorganisms. This will help to form the basis of the cleaning and fogging frequency requirements.

6.3.1.8 Doorways and hatches

Air movement through doorways can be significantly different from that in other parts of the factory and can cause greater microbiological risk as a result. The balance of air between air input and extraction as well as temperature differential, people and equipment movement can all impact on the rate of air movement sufficient to cause microorganisms to be present in significant numbers.

6.3.2 *Waste disposal*

The procedures for the removal of food and packaging waste must be clearly understood and implemented to minimise the risks that may arise from microbiological or foreign body hazards. All waste containers must be clearly marked and easily identifiable from all other food containers. They must be captive to the high-risk area and used in conjunction with a tipping mechanism or practice that empties into the low-risk side of the barrier. The movement of the waste containers must also be carefully controlled to prevent contamination. This disposal area must be physically segregated from other parts of the factory and must be easy to clean. Cleaning and sanitising of waste bins and any associated equipment must form part of the hygiene regime.

6.3.3 *Cleaning*

6.3.3.1 Cleaning activity

Cleaning activity must be assessed in the context not just of the activity itself but also of the other operations in the vicinity, for example food handling, hand washing and movement through the cleaning area. Drift of aerosols through the environment to neighbouring areas or rooms could also be a source of contamination.

The aim should be to minimise the use of water throughout the factory to reduce the opportunity for microbial growth and subsequent contamination of foodstuffs. This is particularly relevant in the high-risk environment.

The target should be to eliminate the use of high-pressure hoses anywhere within the factory. If anything other than mains water pressure is used, then a full microbiological risk assessment should be carried out.

6.3.3.2 Cleaning systems

Dispensing of diluted chemicals via a pumped ring main is an excellent way to facilitate cleaning activity. Procedures to measure and record chemical strength are essential to support cleaning efficiency. Microbiological testing of diluted cleaning chemicals, particularly neutral detergents, is worthwhile, as it is possible that there are harbourage points for microbial growth to occur. In a personally observed situation, a dilute chemical tank with no agitation resulted in stratification and growth of Enterobacteriaceae in the tank. Improved agitation linked with regular cleaning and microbiological testing helped to resolve the issue.

The connection points within the factory can become contaminated with bacteria and they too need to be part of a cleaning and sanitising system.

Any changes to the ring main design need to be reviewed to ensure that the pipework has no dead legs or that sections of the system have low flow. Maintenance of an accurate diagram of the ring main network with all dispensing points clearly marked as well as identification at the point of use is important, together with a sampling programme from the drop points linked to this diagram. This approach applies to the potable water supply in the factory.

Hoses and hand grips for the ring main must be stored correctly and form part of the cleaning regime.

Any hoses used on the ring main should be checked to ensure that they are fit for the purpose; a hose that is too long and drags along the floor or is too short and causes operatives to "extend" the hose by various means is not acceptable.

Motorised floor scrubbers are not recommended for use in the high-risk environment during food preparation as they create aerosols from the brushes and from the air exhaust from the vacuum used to collect the water and débris from the floor.

The design of tray washers within the high-risk cleaning bay needs careful consideration to prevent this piece of equipment from becoming a source of contamination rather than an effective cleaning system. The infeed design must be evaluated to prevent the build-up of contamination, and also the contaminated infeed and clean outfeed must be used by different personnel. Regular descaling and routine maintenance need to be carefully managed to prevent any drop in efficiency of the cleaning process. Chemical dosing and temperature must be monitored (see Fig. 6.2). These considerations must also apply to other equipment used in the high-risk cleaning bay, e.g. depositor washer.

6.3.3.3 Depth of clean

Deep cleaning is defined as the cleaning and sanitising of equipment to a defined level of access, whereby equipment is dismantled to the point where all food contact surfaces can be cleaned and sanitised, as well as potential points of ingress (9). The shaft and sealing glands of mixer would be typical examples. Deep cleaning is carried out using a detailed cleaning procedure, which describes the dismantling process supported by diagrams and/or photographs, equipment required, resource needed to complete the work and safety requirements.

The frequency of clean will depend on a variety of factors; for example, depositors are deep cleaned after every production run whilst conveyors may be cleaned once a day. Typically, this type of cleaning is carried out when there is little or no production activity.

WEEK ENDING FACTORY:					Target >1.1 = 1% Quatdet		
Location (please state location)	Sun	Mon	Tues	Wed	Thurs	Fri	Sat
Low risk cookline							
1							
2							
High risk cookline							
1							
2							
Soak tanks (utensils/pipework)							
1							
2							
3							
Protec sanitiser outlets							
In vessel cleaning area							
Above soak tanks							
By rollers - Clean area							
End of tinwash - by hand basin							
End of tinwash - hose from chemical unit							
Trays							
1							
2							
3							
4							
5							
6							
7							
8							
9							
10							
11							
12							
13							
14							

Fig. 6.2. Example of chart used to monitor solution strength of utensil dips

Washdown cleaning is used to clean and sanitise only those surfaces that can be easily accessed without major dismantling of equipment – for example, tables and conveyor surfaces. This may be carried out at break times during production activity.

6.3.3.4 Cleaning resource

Cleaning operations have not traditionally been given the same attention as production activities in terms of efficiencies – that is, the time and resource necessary to clean any defined area or equipment. For the maintenance of a clean environment, this information is essential to allow the appropriate cleaning intervals and work prioritisation to be carried out effectively by the hygiene management team.

Cleaning procedures should include a reference to man-hours to complete the task to a defined standard as well as personal protective equipment, chemicals required, cleaning equipment and specific safety precautions.

Planning of cleaning activities should be as sophisticated as any production plan and should be capable of allowing the hygiene management team to change priorities and run through a number of different options and priorities for cleaning. Most of the reputable companies selling cleaning chemicals offer some support on cleaning procedures and training, but there is little help to maximise the efficiency of the hygiene team in terms of time and resource available. Cleaning personnel need to be carefully selected, trained and given clear standards to achieve. Failure of any of these criteria can have serious consequences.

6.3.3.5 Footwear washing

Work at Campden and Chorleywood Food Research Association has indicated that the cleanliness and wetness of footwear has a significant impact on microbiological build-up in the environment (11). Cleaning of footwear using bespoke washers is reasonably effective provided due consideration is given to the siting of the washer to prevent contamination of the local environment or clothing of the person using the machine by droplets of water that may contain bacteria. The unit should be situated at least 2 metres away from any food handling areas. Manual cleaning at a separate, physically segregated area is a widely used acceptable practice. Either cleaning method must be followed by a sanitising stage.

A well documented management system to control the issue and replacement of footwear is required to support the cleaning regime.

The design of the footwear used in all parts of the factory must be carefully considered in terms of material – plastic or rubber as well as tread pattern. Colour coding between low risk and high risk is also vital.

Storage systems for footwear in the high-risk environment must facilitate cleaning and drying of the footwear as well as being intrinsically cleanable itself.

The use of disposable overshoes is not recommended as they can wear out very quickly, resulting in entrapment of water and or foodstuff between the shoe and the overshoe. Plastic clip-on types that can be cleaned, sanitised and re-used may be acceptable in certain circumstances – for instance, when the workforce needs to be increased for short periods of high production.

6.3.4 Fabric

6.3.4.1 Drain design

Good design can significantly reduce the microbiological risk. Droplet production from loose, rattling drain covers when equipment or food containers are wheeled over the cover has been implicated in product contamination. The correct sealing of the drain channel into the floor to prevent build-up of water and residue behind the channel is essential (see Fig. 6.3). The fall of the drain and the sizing of drains downstream must also be borne in mind. Drain covers must be made of a hygienic material such as stainless steel or heavy-duty plastic. Ease of removal of drain covers is also essential to ensure that they can be easily inspected and cleaned. The sizing of drains in relation to peak flow is vital to prevent backing up and flooding of the floor and the subsequent transfer of microorganisms over the floor and possibly onto food. If this is not achievable in the short term, then management of the times that water is put to drain must be used as an alternative.

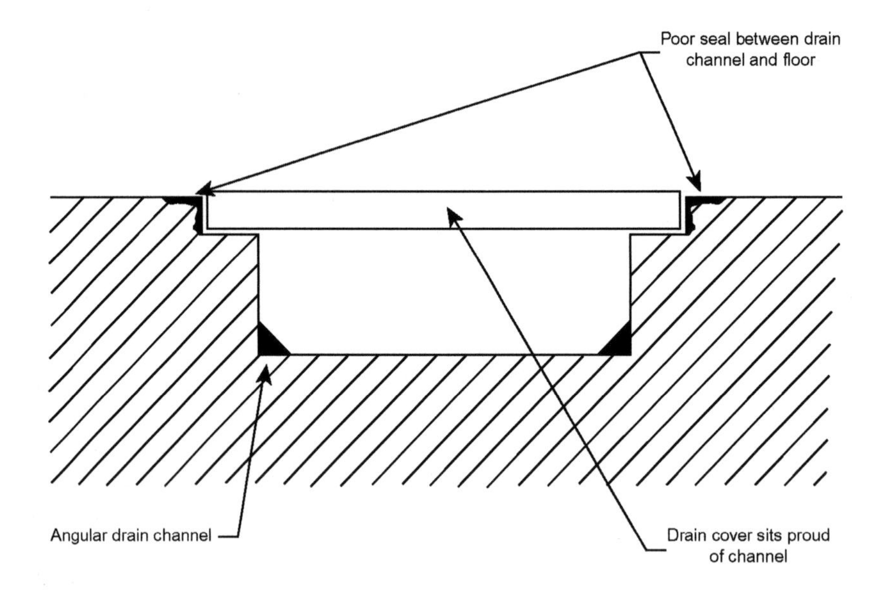

Fig. 6.3. Microbiological harbourage points in drains

Drains that are not in use must be capped, although they should be easily opened for inspection. Where catchpots are fitted to drains, an emptying procedure must be defined to reduce contamination risks. Any pipes running from equipment or fittings must be run into the drain channel and not left to flow over the floor.

The jointing of the drain channel to the floor must be given due care. Poor design and application of sealant material can create a reservoir between the two, which can result in the build-up of microorganisms.

Regular drain cleaning by a specialist contractor every 6 months is recommended to reduce the risk of blockage and subsequent backing up of foul water into the food handling areas. Care should be taken to ensure that the contractor does not himself become a source of contamination.

Routine maintenance of wheeled equipment should be carried out to ensure that the wheels and casters turn easily, to minimise the wear and tear to the drain assembly.

Movement of large items of equipment can cause undue pressure on the drains and therefore induce a weak point that will become a harbourage for microorganisms.

6.3.4.2 Hand washing

The siting of a hand-wash station is crucial not only to ensure that all staff are encouraged to use these facilities but that the hand washing and particularly the drying of hands does not itself pose a risk to product. Consequently, the hand-wash station should be physically separated from the main food handling area and preferably with a localised air extraction system. There is some evidence that hand washing should be done before putting on high-risk clothing followed by addition of sanitising agent, usually an alcohol water mix, without an intermediate hand wash.

Use of an invisible UV marker applied to the hands prior to washing and then checked using a UV lamp after washing can be a useful tool to ensure that staff get the message on effective hand washing.

The same material might also be used in the cleaning area to assess cross-contamination routes and, having identified them, eliminate them from the workplace.

The application of sanitiser can be encouraged by using automatic stations linked to a turnstile – the turnstile will only operate if both hands are put into a chamber with an infrared sensor that dispenses a fixed volume of alcohol mist onto the hands. This can be linked to a counter. Traditional swabs taken from the "clean" hands of personnel can also be used to check for Enterobacteriaceae, *Escherichia coli* and *Staphylococcus aureus*. Any counts registered must be communicated to the individual and appropriate counselling or training given, which must be recorded.

6.3.4.3 Movement of food

Within any food handling environment, food must be moved from chill to the cooking system, to the product assembly line or packing line. During this transit process, the risk of contamination must be minimised by covering the food container and ensuring that transit routes do not come close to cleaning activities.

The use of wheeled containers, racks, bins, etc., to move foodstuffs can cause the creation of droplets on wet floors, which in turn may contaminate the product or the operative moving the container. Wheels moving over drain covers can cause vibration, which in turn can create droplets. Poorly fitting drain channels can harbour water and microorganisms between the drain channel and the flooring material, which may then be squeezed out onto the floor when items are wheeled over the drain and thus provide a contamination route. To reduce this risk, it is advisable not to use the bottom shelf of a cooling rack and to ensure that the design of the rack shields the product from any splashing. Similarly, product in containers should be covered. Subsequently, work flow designed to minimise the movement of material must be considered.

6.3.4.4 Cleaning equipment

The design of cleaning equipment must be given careful consideration, taking into account the working conditions, the cleanability of the equipment, the training required to use it and cost. For example, a squeegee used to remove water from the floor must have an integral handle with a solid rubber blade (foam rubber types are not acceptable as they can harbour microorganisms within the structure of the rubber, which may be difficult to eradicate). There are many examples of cleaning equipment that are not suitable for the food industry, e.g. cleaning brushes that do not have bonded bristles, which can pose a foreign body hazard and provide harbourage for microorganisms.

The inclusion of Microban® – a bactericidal agent that can be incorporated into certain kinds of plastic and rubber – into cleaning equipment (handles, fixtures for handles, blades, etc.) is an extra safeguard to be considered.

Colour coding of the equipment must also be used to reduce the risk of cleaning equipment being moved from the low-risk area into the high-risk environment. Colour coding should also be used for items used in specific tasks, e.g. cleaning up waste or vegetarian only areas. Ease of use should not be underestimated as a factor in equipment selection. If it is too heavy, it will discourage effective use and may cause repetitive strain injury. Handles and grips need to be appropriate for the job – handles that are too fine or too thick cause difficulty in gripping.

The effective storage of cleaning equipment must form part of hygiene management thinking. Inadequate storage results in equipment being stored in uncontrolled environments, e.g. personal lockers, rather than being kept within the high-risk area. The storage area or receptacle needs to be well ventilated to allow the equipment to dry between uses.

Cleaning equipment must be incorporated into the cleaning schedules to ensure that it does not itself become a source of contamination. An example would be a hosepipe that has been heavily used without soaking in a bactericide after use, which can become a source of contamination. This must be documented just like all other cleaning activities. All cleaning equipment must be identified and numbered to ensure that cleaning records can be corroborated. The use of plastic items, e.g. shovels, needs to be controlled to assess their condition as they can become scratched and scored relatively easily, which may pose a foreign body and microbiological hazard.

Apart from cleaning utensils themselves, tools used to strip equipment prior to cleaning, such as spanners and screwdrivers, must meet the same hygienic design requirements. They must also be dedicated to the high-risk area. Tool boxes can be a major problem once they get wet and become sources of microbial contamination.

More specialised tools that may be kept outside the high-risk area must be sanitised at the point of entry to the high-risk area. Engineers and contractors must be made to understand and follow the procedure. If they fail to comply, then suitable action should be taken.

6.3.4.5 Consumable items

Alcohol-impregnated wipes or hand sprayers are recommended for general use on conveyors and tables for production times. All cloths should be used once only.

If rubber gloves and plastic aprons are used, they must be checked for microbiological loading. They must be subject to a defined procedure for transfer to the high-risk area, as must all other consumable items, including, for example, paper towels for hand-wash stations.

6.3.4.6 Clothing

Clothes must be designed to ensure that there are no loose threads or that fraying does not occur; there should be no external pockets, and popper fasteners should be used. Elasticated cuffs should also be used to reduce foreign body contamination. Overalls must be designed to fit the people.

Overalls dragging on the floor or flapping into product and rolled up sleeves are not acceptable. Overalls must be changed if they get soiled or wet during working time and for every shift irrespective of the place of work

– low- or high-risk environments. There must be sufficient clean overalls available to cope with accidental spillages as well as the routine daily changes. The use of a clothing management system is recommended to ensure that overalls are cleaned at the designated frequency and that a replacement scheme can be operated effectively.

A system of colour coding for all the different activities within the operation needs to be incorporated into the clothing design, i.e. separate colours for low-risk food handlers, high-risk food handlers, engineers, hygiene low and high risk and other duties, e.g. toilet cleaning. Disposable overalls should be used only *in extremis* – periods of high activity, for example.

6.3.4.7 Laundry

The laundry provider should be audited as any other supplier of food or service. Segregation of overalls within the facility should, as a minimum, be between food, non-food, high-risk and low-risk. Dedicated containers for carrying protective garments for the site should be provided to reduce risks of cross contamination.

There should be a record of temperature achieved in the wash process, which must exceed 72 °C for 2 minutes. A Hazard Analysis and Critical Control Point system should be in operation within the laundry. An appropriate cleaning agent should be used – no perfume or residue should be left on the garments.

Laundry building fabric should match that required in the food industry. Post-wash segregation and individually wrapped high-risk garments are all part of the requirements.

6.3.4.8 'Clean as you go'

'Clean as you go' is a much abused term, but should mean the removal of food débris as soon as possible after spillage to reduce cross contamination and microbiological risks as well as to prevent slips and falls. The tools that have been designated for the task should be cleaned and sanitised after use. Failure to clean and sanitise the tools can cause as much of a problem as the spillage. Hand washing must follow any clean-up operation without touching anything in the interim. This operation should be carried out by personnel who are not food handlers. Using packaging, food handling equipment or anything other than the designated equipment is not acceptable. The food spill should be cleaned up, preferably without the use of water – swilling waste down the nearest drain is not good practice, nor is the vigorous use of a squeegee. The reduction of risk from droplet formation from clean as you go is important to ensure that this process itself does not compromise the integrity of the product.

If spillage is the consequence of poor equipment design or poor maintenance, the causes must be addressed. If the spillage is a continuous source of extra work, the procedures will rapidly fall down.

Training must be given to ensure that these principles are applied at all times.

6.3.4.9 Transfer of items into high risk

The following equipment is available for the transfer of items into the high-risk environment. Each technology has advantages and weaknesses and should be assessed for each factory and the range of materials to be transferred.

UV tunnels consist of a conveyor enclosed by stainless steel housing containing UV light emitting tubes, which are covered in plastic film to reduce the risk of glass contamination if a tube breaks. The tubes surround the conveyor to ensure 360 degree coverage of the item as it moves along the conveyor. A UV tunnel has the advantage of being a dry sanitising system that will penetrate some forms of clear colourless packaging. However, it can be prone to shadowing, which reduces the microbiocidal effect, and there is some temperature increase on the surface of the item passing through the tunnel.

A sanitising spray containing an appropriate microbiocide is one of the simplest forms of transfer equipment, usually consisting of a spray bar surrounding an open mesh conveyor. The advantage is simplicity, but this must be balanced by the need to ensure that contact time for the microbiocide is sufficient and that water is introduced into the high-risk area, although the latter may be overcome by using alcohol as the sanitiser. Sanitisers include chlorine, quaternary ammonium compounds, ozone in solution and possibly hydrogen peroxide. A simple dip tank using the above bactericides can also be used.

Other options include ozone tunnels, which have good microbiocidal effects although health and safety issues must be considered.

A steam tunnel has been used in some instances, although again the system introduces water into the high-risk environment. This method also warms up the product.

Customer concern has effectively eliminated the use of X-rays, although its use for the transfer of packaging into the high-risk environment may be worth considering. This method is widely used in the treatment of medical supplies. The safety of personnel operating this type of equipment must be evaluated and all appropriate measures taken.

6.3.5 *Factory fabric*

6.3.5.1 Services

Typical examples of services include compressed air and electrical supplies and water at the cook lines and drop points for chemical dispensing systems.

The provision of services within the food handling environment should be situated overhead rather than under equipment, to reduce soiling and damage and aid visual inspection. Care should be exercised to ensure minimal physical risks at the same time.

6.3.5.2 Pipework

All pipework – drain pipes, CIP lines, mains water, hot water – must be appropriate in that there are no dead ends or conflicts in the directions of the flow, and the material of construction is appropriate for the application, e.g. stainless steel grade 316 for CIP pipework, welding to be ground smooth and use of International Dairy Federation (IDF) fittings, etc. There are specific standards on pipework and valvery design. The pipework should have easily removed sections for inspection to assess efficiency of flow and scale build-up.

Cleaning procedures for the external surfaces of the services must also be in place.

6.3.5.3 Cabling and air lines

Conduits and cable coatings can become harbourage points for water and microorganisms. Conduits should be positioned away from potential sources of contamination, vertically mounted and sealed against water ingress wherever it is situated. If cabling is run to equipment, it must be kept in good condition as any damage to the cable covering can allow water ingress and hence become a source of contamination.

When equipment has to be moved to a cleaning area, the cabling must be properly supported to prevent it from dragging on the floor.

Compressed air lines must be kept off the floor, so the design of the equipment and the provision of such services must be given due consideration.

6.3.5.4 Water supplies

The factory water supply should come from a treated supply either directly off the mains or from an intermediate holding tank. The holding tank should be treated with a secondary microbiocidal process, such as chlorine, ozone or UV light. Limits should be set and monitored frequently (12,13).

At no point should taps or outlets be common to operatives in high-risk and low-risk areas – for example, around open cooking vessels – to minimise the risk of cross contamination.

Accurate diagrams of water supply lines must be maintained.

Regular audits of pipework are necessary to ensure that no dead legs have arisen or stretches of pipework have become starved of supply, which can cause settlement of sediment over time.

In all cases, fittings should be of a hygienic design using welded pipes where possible with simple tap handles and food standard seals.

If any water supply point has not been used for a significant period of time, it must be run for at least 10 minutes prior to use to ensure that it has been properly flushed.

Cold water pipes can be a source of contamination in cooking areas where condensation is prevalent; therefore cold water pipes should not pass over open vessels.

Water hardness must be measured on a regular basis to ensure that detergency efficacy is maintained and boiler elements do not become furred up, which in turn may reduce the efficiency of water heating and hence factory water temperature.

Build-up of calciferous scale can occur quickly in frequently used items of equipment; cleaning using acid based chemicals should be employed on a predetermined basis to ensure that this is kept under control.

A microbiological sampling and testing programme must be in place for the potable supply from the point of use. Recent work on *Cryptosporidium* in mains water would suggest that a filtration system for occasions when a boiled water notice is issued by the supplying water company would be appropriate. The use of UV light treatment for this purpose may be an option pending further research.

6.3.5.5 Hot water supplies

A detailed knowledge of all boiler water treatment chemicals is required not just for legal obligations but in the context of potential food contamination.

Maintaining hot water temperature during peak demand is key to effective cleaning and hand washing. Water that is too hot, particularly at hand wash systems, discourages its use and creates excessive condensation.

6.3.5.6 Floors

Floor finish needs to reflect the need for personnel safety but must be balanced by the ease of clean and waterproof finish (14). Biofilm build-up on the floor can be a significant source of contamination over the course of production activity. The fall of the floor to ensure that there is no standing water and that it runs to drain are crucial. Joint design must ensure that a tough chemically resistant water join is used. Badly pitted and cracked floors are not acceptable.

6.3.5.7 Walls and ceilings

Wall and ceiling finishes must be smooth, with curved covings to kerbs or floor. They must be impervious to water and be resistant to the cleaning and sanitising chemicals used. A white finish is preferable to aid the assessment of visual cleanliness.

Any indications of mould growth either on the panels or on jointing material must be removed promptly and the cause of the growth – for example poor air extraction – identified and eliminated (15,16).

6.3.5.8 Pits

Ovens and weighing platforms are often sited in shallow pits in the factory floor. The design of the pit must ensure that there is sufficient drainage and the rim of the hole is sealed to ensure that there are no cracks for microbial attachment. The fall of the floor within the pit should also be adequate to prevent stagnation of water or residue. There must be a safe system for lifting the weighing platform or oven ramps to allow access for cleaning and maintenance.

6.3.5.9 Light fittings

Ceiling-mounted light fittings should be accessible from outside the high-risk area wherever possible – for example via a roof void – to reduce the risk of glass contamination. They should also be sealed to prevent ingress of condensation from the high-risk area. There should be a regular programme of maintenance, with comprehensive records to support any work.

6.3.5.10 Doors

Doors must be self-closing and have hygienically designed handles with a smooth hygienic finish. Door handles must be part of the routine cleaning and sanitising regime. There is some evidence that *Staphylococcus* species build-up on door handles is relatively rapid on the doors of chills that have a high activity level. Materials used for sealing the door surround must be easily cleaned, inspected on a regular basis and replaced as part of the planned plant maintenance system. The integrity of the door seals for fire doors, either to other areas of the factory or to the exterior, must be maintained to prevent pest and microbiological ingress. Doors of this kind should be protected with an alarm and/or a ceramic bolt to prevent abuse. The inspection of these points must be carried out regularly and recorded. Any breach of the security of doors into the high-risk area must be investigated and corrective action recorded.

6.3.6 Other factors

6.3.6.1 People

There is a wide range of activities that are required to ensure that the risks identified within this chapter are minimised. The controls identified are only as effective as the people who carry them out. Selection of the right people for each role is essential. Whilst relevant paper qualifications are important, the attitude of the individual is key. Personnel must have the enthusiasm, dedication and confidence to maintain and improve the control systems. It will only take one disenchanted individual to undermine the hard work of the rest of the team. Consequently, monitoring morale and giving the right support to both the team and the individual are essential. Setting clear objectives linked to regular feedback on performance will help to motivate the team.

6.3.6.2 Plant rooms

Rooms where air conditioning plant, refrigeration plant, boilers, etc., are installed must not be accessible directly from the food handling areas. These rooms can have high air movement, with consequent relatively rapid dust build-up. They should be cleaned using dry methods to reduce the build-up of yeasts and mould spores and discourage pest infestation.

6.3.7 Operational concerns

The order of manufacture within the high-risk areas can affect the maintenance of a clean environment in a number of ways. The number of changeovers between products can affect the amount of cleaning required and the timing of that cleaning activity and with it the risk of cross contamination. It is therefore necessary to minimise product changeovers, rationalise the order of product manufacture – for example, move from vegetarian to meat-based products and check on cleaning times in relation to manufacturing requirements; there must be sufficient time for cleaning and sanitising of all equipment between production runs. If there is inadequate time, then additional equipment must be found or the order of manufacture must be defined to ensure that sufficient cleaning time is available.

Specific requirements must be communicated to the production planning function so that times, priorities and order of manufacture are followed. There must be sufficient resource available within the team to ensure that cleaning activities – routine cleaning, deep cleaning, clean as you go and intermediate line cleaning – are carried out and that review and training procedures are in place to ensure that standards are maintained. Engineering work must also be regulated to ensure that a clean environment is maintained. Equipment that is to be maintained must be moved to a quarantine area prior to the work being carried out and a suitable return to use procedure put in place to ensure that equipment is handed over to the hygiene team for cleaning and sanitising. This should include a foreign body assessment. As in all other cases, this system must be fully documented.

Changes to shift patterns can have an effect on cleaning activity – for instance, the demand for specific equipment may change and hence the timing of the cleaning activity will change. The presence of contractors can pose particular problems and challenges as they may have little concept of the disciplines of a food factory. Building contractors particularly can be a challenge.

Communication on requirements must be given to the contractor at the time of the award of work, as well as to those staff who will come on site. This is best achieved by direct verbal communication backed up by written requirements, which must be signed and acknowledged by the contractor. Regular monitoring of their activities is required and inappropriate actions must be corrected promptly. If they continue to transgress they must be asked to leave the site. There can be no compromise on the clean environment.

Without detailing material intake procedures, the condition of vehicles and the containers for the delivery of materials to the factory can be a source of ingress of microorganisms, pests and foreign bodies (17). Inspection of vehicles and containers prior to offloading will help in this respect, as well as forming part of the quality assurance system.

Communication of requirements, the reasons why and the consequences of doing or not doing things need to be clearly communicated to all members of the team at all levels.

6.3.8 Trend analysis

To keep an environment clean, the use of data generated from routine and investigative work needs to be evaluated on a regular basis. This information can be based on luminescence (ATP) swab results, traditional microbiological swab results (TVC, Enterobacteriaceae, *Staphylococcus, E. coli, Listeria*) (see Fig. 6.4), audit scores or staff attendance levels. For example, engineering work and planned plant maintenance records, as well as breakdown logs, should also be used. Data on production activity – not just the number of units produced but the number of product changeovers made, shift patterns, number of trainees or recently recruited employees on the line – should all be evaluated.

Week Commencing:

Swab No.	Swab Point	Category	Date	Time	Status (clean, in use, etc.)	Any related product?	Signature
106	Terlet product outlet pipe, thread	EP					
109	Potato bin inside lid	EP					
108	Leider potato nozzle	EP					
104	Leider product pipe, RCM1	EP					
110	Chain conveyor, line 2	EP					
169	Leider product pipe, RCM2	EP					
143	Scale pan	EP					
116	Butcher Boy flaps	EH					
141	Transfer pipe internal surface (ex dip)	EP					
146	Film, packaging						
147	Work station, line 3	EP					
170	Potato nozzle	EP					
112	Sealing tool in storage	EP					
171	Telephone	EH					
173	Packing line conveyor	EH					
163	Component chiller, door handle	EH					
174	Stainless steel bucket, cookline	EP					
175	Vessel, inside surface	EP					
176	Depositor, pipework	EP					
135	Depositor, piston barrel	EP					
153	Cleaning brush ex sanitiser dip	EP					
197	Engineers tools						
177	Digi probe	EP					
154	Food tin, in storage	EP					
156	Tin wash outfeed rollers	EP					
178	Transfer pipework, flexible connection	EP					
158	Transfer pump, inside housing	EP					
159	Open vat transfer pipework	EP					
179	Mashed potato scoop	EP					
180	Finished product chiller, door handle	EH					
146	Food scoop	EP					
181	Mixer paddles	EP					
182	Lift control buttons	EH					
183	Evaporator	EH					
	Hygiene 0500 hrs	EH					

Key: EH = environmental swab - hygiene team
EP = environmental swab - production team

Fig. 6.4. Weekly swabbing rota

Changes to process should be checked, e.g. the introduction of equipment into a critical part of the factory. The timescale element needs to be used in a number of ways – for example by shift, day of the week, monthly or by year – to ensure that possible trends are detected. Whilst a trend may be perceived, corroborating evidence from carry out trials should be sought to support the hypothesis. Factory environments and working practices can change very rapidly and interact in quite subtle ways, so cross-checking is always a sensible practice.

Commercial implications should not be ignored – undue delay can prove costly; sometimes a shotgun approach to remedial action for a given situation may be the optimal approach, followed by an investigation to identify specific causes.

There are a number of software packages available to facilitate the analyses.

6.3.9 Training

If there is a single common factor to the success or otherwise of maintaining a clean environment, it has to be the delivery of a sustainable training programme. The development of written procedures and work instructions with training matrices to match should form the basis of the system. Trainers need to have been given the requisite instructional skills. An assessment of the training needs and a system to monitor the efficiency of the programme are essential. The use of a nationally recognised training scheme, e.g. National Vocational Qualifications (NVQ), at levels one and two, would be appropriate for most operatives. The delivery of the training does not necessarily require elaborate facilities, but it does need good preparation and presentation.

A clear and concise set of objectives that define the scope of the training and the desired outcome is required initially.

6.3.10 Strategy

There are many elements to risk control and prevention. To obtain the best from the systems that have been developed it can be useful to look at the culture of the team, the department and factory. Are there clear targets? Are the teams goal-oriented? Is there supportive interaction with other elements, e.g. production and hygiene teams? Is the team inward-looking or resistant to change, or do they have an `us and them' attitude. Consequently, strategies can be developed at quite different levels. Regardless of the culture within the organisation, working out what is achievable as a team and in the context of business and customers requirements is a very constructive exercise (18).

Having decided what makes the teams tick, it is essential to be clear about what is to be achieved – producing safe food is not enough; it needs to be more specific. Achievable targets must be set with time scales and the package must be sold to the respective elements of the team. Strategy must be documented and progress reviewed against it at regular intervals. The strategy can be changed if this would improve progress (19). Sticking rigidly to an approach in the face of evidence that indicates that it is not working does not benefit anyone. A support function such as a Food Technologist or Quality Assurance role must be able to influence others who may have different goals. Good preparation with a clear strategy will go a long way towards convincing the team that maintaining a clean environment is important for everyone.

The information should also be shared with the customers, who may have their own ideas about cleaning. Retailers will have their own guidelines and codes of practice, so it would be sensible to couch the strategy in terms that reflect customer needs.

The construction of the strategy must involve all the key influencers within the operation. It may not always be obvious who they are, as job title and seniority should not be the sole criteria used.

Observe who plays the dominant influencing roles in meetings – this may not be the person who talks the most, rather the one who makes things happen.

Having spent a significant proportion of the time in preparation, the presentation of the strategy to all identified parties to ensure they buy into this approach is vital. Whether this is done via a formal large-scale presentation or a series of one-to-one meetings, the selling of the strategy and the consequent commitment of the individuals is worth taking time over. Enthusiasm, an energetic approach and good organisational skills will all help to convince the team that you are serious about maintaining a clean environment.

References

1. Anon. *Microbiological guidelines for some ready to eat foods sampled, at the point of sale: an expert opinion from the Public Health Laboratory Service.* PHLS Microbiology Digest, 13 (1), 41-3. 1996.

2. Anon. *Development and use of microbiological criteria for foods.* Food Science Technology Today, 11 (3), 137-77. 1997.

3. *Effective Microbiological Sampling of Food Processing Environments Guideline No. 20.* Campden and Chorleywood Research Association. 1999.

4. Anon. *Guideline for Good Hygienic Practice in the Manufacture of Chilled Foods, 3rd edition.* Chilled Foods Association. 1997.

5. Anon. *Draft Hazard Analysis and Critical Control Point (HACCP) System and Guidelines for its Application.* ALINORM 97/13A Appendix II. 1997.

6. *Guidelines for the Design and Construction of Floors for Food Production Areas.* Technical Manual No. 40. Campden and Chorleywood Research Association. 1993.

7. *Guideline for the Design and Construction of Walls, Ceilings and Services for Food Production Areas.* Technical Manual No. 44. Campden and Chorleywood Research Association. 1994.

8. Brown K.L., Burfoot D. *Process Equipment for Localised Food Cooling.* Project 31103. Research Summary Sheet 81. 1999.

9. Anon. *A Practical Guide To The Disinfection of Food Processing Factories and Equipment Using Fogging.* Silsoe Research Institute. 1998.

10. *Hygienic Design of Food Processing Equipment.* Technical Manual No. 7. Campden and Chorleywood Research Association. 1993.

11. Taylor J. *Hand and Footwear Hygiene: An Investigation to Define Best Practice.* Project 35461. Research Summary Sheet 11. 1998.

12. *Water Quality for the Food Industry: An Introductory Manual Guideline No. 21.* Campden and Chorleywood Research Association. 1998.

13. *Guideline for Drinking Water Quality.* Geneva, World Health Organisation. 1993.

14. *Hard Floor Cleaning Manual.* Dowding and Plummer Ltd, Stockfield Road, Acocks Green, Birmingham. B27 6AP. 2000.

15. Anon. *Guidelines on Air Quality Standards for the Food Industry.* Guideline No. 12. Campden and Chorleywood Research Association. 1996.

16. *Guideline for the Design and Construction of Walls, Ceilings and Services for Food Production Areas.* Technical Manual No. 44. Campden and Chorleywood Research Association. 1994.

17. Wallin P., Haycock P. *Foreign Body Prevention, Detection and Control.* London, Blackie Academic and Professional. 1998.

18. *Listing of Codes of Practice Applicable to Foods.* London, Institute of Food Science and Technology. 1993.

19. Anon. *Food and Drink – Good Manufacturing Practice: A Guide to its Responsible Management.* Institute of Food Science and Technology. London. 1998.

Web sites

Bristol University: http://www.bristol.ac.uk

Campden and Chorleywood Food Research Association:
http://www.campden.co.uk

Food Standards Agency: http://www.foodstandards.gov.uk.

Institute of Food Science and Technology: http://www.ifst.org

Institute Food Research: http://www.ifrn.bbsrc.ac.uk

Silsoe Research Institute: http://www.sri.bbsrc.ac.uk

7. DETERMINING THE QUALITY

Margaret Stevenson

7.1 Introduction

Food processing is becoming an important and fast-growing industry as many more ready meals are purchased. This makes attention to all aspects of food safety and quality an absolute must and anyone preparing food for public consumption must adhere to all codes of practices set out under the Food Safety Act.

The adage "You can make a bad product with good raw materials but you can't make a good product with bad raw materials" has never been more relevant than in today's ready meals market.

The sheer level of complexity of the products available offers so many choices and challenges. Ready meals manufacturers are aware that misjudgments can be made at any stage and result in quality erosion. What is quality: a question to be answered within the boundaries of individual business and its requirements of which there are many different deliberations.

Cook-chill products, frozen meals, and snack pots, as examples, will all have to have quality standards built into the process to ensure consistency, and gain recognition through customer loyalty to a company's products.

This chapter will lead us through a very subjective area and will try to give some real examples of how to bring objectivity to the term "quality", starting with how to determine the quality required through to measuring quality and a closing summary.

- Determine the quality required
- Setting the standards
- Value for money
- Fitness for consumption
- Giving the customer what they require
- Conforming to all legal requirements
- Analytical standards, either in-house or independent testing (chemical/microbiological)

7.2 Determine the Quality Required

In determining the consistency required for quality, all personnel must be trained to understand quality. Training enhances all departments of manufacture, where each should set standards and procedures to be trained against. Quality must be a linked process starting from the first concept to the final distribution. Product quality standards must be set that adhere to agreed specifications. Starting with raw materials, a consistent standard must be set within the specification agreement. This would apply to all materials in the process of manufacture. When all parameters have been achieved, reliability of manufacture should be achievable at the beginning. Constancy of taste must be a priority and processes put in place to ensure that this is achievable. For any product to survive the market place it has to attract customers.

Long-term product success will depend on customer satisfaction, price, safety, and the knowledge that, whenever a meal is purchased, the taste and presentation will be what is expected. To achieve this level of quality, the manufacturer should deal only with reputable suppliers, who in turn have the necessary standards that are required under the Food Safety Act; supplier evaluation/ ratings audits carried out by the vendor would be advisable. To achieve the stability of quality required it must be achieved at the start; it cannot be put in later. When the correct approach is set at the beginning, it will save time, energy, and money. These are general guidelines that must be followed, whether a large manufacturing process or a small concern. In consideration of setting standards, they must be realistic and achievable within any specification for the product to be made.

7.3 Quality Policy and Objectives

A quality policy commits any organisation to achieve requirements and the scope for continual improvement. It is a key document against which any quality system can be reviewed. All businesses must have a quality statement, incorporating standards that the manufacturer will achieve regarding quality, safety to the consumer and compliance with all statutory laws under the Food Safety Act, and any Codes of Practice that may be required by the customer. It is also a statement that the manufacturer will comply with the agreed specifications for the procurement of raw materials and the production of any ready meal for sale to the public.

The following requirements should also be included:

- Manufacture safe products to agreed quality standards.
- Only use specified raw materials from approved suppliers.
- Operate to strict hygiene controls.

- Meet all legal requirements for the manufacture, labelling and packaging of products.
- Actively involve enforcement authorities in order to maintain the highest operating standards.
- Provide appropriate training to all staff handling food and review regularly.
- Achieve and maintain a manufacturing standard consistent with any accredited status (EFSIS, BRC, etc.).
- Management reviews for continual improvement.
- Objectives to be measurable and defined, for customer satisfaction, response time, delivery, productivity, and analysis of customer complaints.
- Good management practice, incorporating foreign body, process, despatch, hygiene, and engineering controls.

Quality and reliability are assets to any business and there is an obligation to the customer to ensure those quality standards are consistently met.

7.4 Setting the Standards

7.4.1 Raw materials

Raw materials must be of a standard such that the achievement of agreed specification is not compromised. The vendor should have specifications against which all raw materials are purchased (these may be a part of individual purchase agreements, rather than separate specifications) and a method of assessment for incoming materials. When importing foods, it is important to define accurately the variety, type, age, etc., of any materials to ensure that the same standard with regard to quality is maintained in each batch. Define a supplier Code of Practice, which should ensure that all suppliers are following the Codes of Practice set by the manufacturer. Evidence of raw material control through recorded documentation can determine that the specification is consistently achievable. It would always be appropriate to have a second source of materials, that would match the quality expected should the need arise, to allow for seasonal changes of components, and to ensure that the second supplier source conforms to the standards laid down.

Through all areas of raw material intake, documented evidence is important should the manufacturer have to defend itself with respect to due diligence in a court of law and will help maintain consistency of the standards and quality expected by the customer.

The safety, quality and composition of delivered materials must be effectively managed through a formalised approach by Supply Management. This must incorporate the provision of supply specifications for all food ingredients and other materials, and the assurance of the standards of the supply source in terms of food safety and hygiene standards.

Inspection and testing regimes for all delivered goods and materials must be devised that conform to supply specifications and relevant food safety standards. Provisions for the management of non-conforming deliveries must be in place.

7.5 Cooking Methods

Cooking improves taste, smell and appearance of food and is thought to improve digestibility. It can also promote the keeping qualities of food by reducing bacteria such as moulds, and yeasts, and others that can cause decay. However, a distinction must be made between cooking and heat treatment to preserve foods. Cooking can be simply defined as the heat treatment of food, which is carried out to improve palatability, digestibility and safety of food. Methods of cook will need to be considered individually, with attention being paid to the effect that differing methods of cook would have on the nutrients within the food, i.e. giving differing quality and consistency of products.

There are several methods of cooking, as shown in Table 7.I.

TABLE 7.I
Cooking methods

Dry heat	Baking, roasting	Cooking in oven or open vessel, which generates hot air and reflected heat.
	Grilling, broiling	Direct heat, either radiation or with some conduction.
Moist heat	Boiling	Cooking in boiling water by conduction
	Steaming	Cooking by direct steam or in a steam heated vessel through conduction and convection
	Pressure cooking	Cooking by steam under pressure, through conduction
	Stewing, simmering	Cooking in water below boiling point through conduction
Hot fat	Frying	Frying food that is completely or partially immersed in heated fat, through conduction
	Braising	Brief frying in shallow fat, followed by stewing, through conduction.
	Microwave	Food subjected to microwave radiation in an oven. This method is heat generation in food.

7.5.1 Moist heat method

This method employs relatively low temperatures; therefore, the destruction of nutrients within the food is low. However, because of the amount of cooking time required for this method, it results in extensive loss of the soluble nutrients into the liquid, especially of vitamin C. Many factors must be taken into consideration with this method as variability can occur: the treatment of food before cook, amount of liquid used and length of cooking time. The exclusion of air and how long the food is to be kept hot will also affect nutrient loss. Placing, e.g., vegetables into boiling water destroys enzymes, which spoil food, but is preferable to putting into cold water and bringing to the boil.

7.5.2 Boiling

The most common method of moist heat is boiling. Because the water has to have a high specific heat, it is efficient and is readily available, making it the most convenient form in which to transmit heat into food.

During development trials, times of cook must be established and standards set on the texture of the components. Consideration must also be given to batch sizes, e.g. components sliced, cubed, peeled, chopped or shredded, when setting cooking times. Treatments such as those mentioned above change the surface area of the components and will set up an enzymic reaction; therefore, these factors will have to be taken into account when determining shelf life and colour. To preserve flavour and texture, a small amount of water and a short cooking time would be preferred. Components that are not peeled can give better flavour, as many of the nutrients do not escape through cooking. Immediate cooling after cooking also preserves flavour and texture. Refreshing vegetables, for example, with cold water at a temperature of between 5 and 10 °C prior to chilling below 2 °C, would also help in preserving colour, texture and flavour.

7.5.3 Steaming

Using steam produced from boiling water reduces contact between food and water. Food cooked by this method loses less soluble matter than when boiled. As cooking time is increased by this method, more ascorbic acid is destroyed. Using steam under pressure increases the temperature at which you can cook. By increasing steam pressure to achieve 120 °C, ascorbic acid is conserved because cooking time is considerably reduced, which is valuable in retaining nutrients of both fruits and vegetables. This method will also help to retain colour, texture and flavour.

7.5.4 Stewing

Stewing is a method of cooking food at temperatures below boiling point, and physicochemical changes to foods occur slower than when boiling. With this method, a considerable loss of soluble matter takes place; however, the advantage of this method is that because of the lower temperatures used, the proteins are presented in a more digestible form. Tough meats would be an ideal choice for this type of cooking method and all liquid expended can be used in the making of, e.g., soups, gravy or dressings. The liquid will have retained the nutrients and flavour from the stewed food, giving an opportunity to make good use of it when considering how the food will eventually be served. Although many fruits are eaten raw, stewing, e.g. of rhubarb or damsons, improves the taste with the inclusion of sugar. Stewing breaks down cellulose in the fruit, and the protein lightly coagulates, as the soluble matter is lost from the cooking liquors of many fruits.

7.5.5 Dry heat

The effect of dry heat will cause colour definition to the surface of food (Maillard reaction). Carbohydrates are affected by heat, and the starch is converted and becomes brown. Breads, pastries, grilled meat, etc., undergo the browning effect, making the food aesthetically attractive.

7.5.6 Deep-pan frying

Deep-pan frying is a very convenient cooking method and particularly useful for high-temperature cooking, enabling rapid cooking of food. Temperatures from 175-200 °C can be achieved, and when food is placed into the fat, the outside becomes crisp and eventually golden brown. This method of cooking is so quick that any nutrient loss is minimal because of the quick seal of the outer part of the component. Strict controls on temperatures must be adhered to when using deep-fat frying to prevent blue smoke haze, which would lead to burning. Colour acceptance of the component would have to be built into product specifications.

7.5.7 Shallow frying

Shallow frying seals the food by immersion into shallow fat and allows cooking without the component sticking to the pan. Cooking is done mainly by direct conductive heat; however, because heat is directed to one side, and unless the components are frequently turned, uneven cooking may be a problem. Cooking times for each side of the component to be cooked would have to be built into the specification, as well as guidelines for texture and colour.

Through either of these methods, fats used must be pure to prevent impurities that may decompose at high temperatures, causing unpleasant taste and odours. Fried foods do absorb some of the fat they are cooked in, which results in an increase of the energy value.

7.5.8 Microwave

Applications for this type of cooking method include, bacon, meat patties and potatoes; drying and pasteurisation of pasta; proving, baking and pasteurisation of bread doughs; freeze drying: blanching; rendering; roasting; setting of meat emulsions; grain; seed and peanut drying; soya bean dehulling; sterilisation.

Cooking food by this method, however, does not colour or develop any crispness but it does allow the food to retain most of the nutrients within it; some believe that it does change flavour. This would provide an ideal method for ready meals for use in hospitals' canteens, restaurants, etc.

7.5.9 Sous vide

The term sous vide comes from French and means 'under vacuum'; the process means that the food is vacuum-packed and cooked in that state at low temperatures. Sometimes it is referred to as pouch cooking, or vacuum cooking. Although the production of cook-chill products by a process involving pasteurisation, chilling and chilled storage prior to reheating has commonly been used for a number of years, sous vide using vacuum packaging of products before pasteurisation is now becoming more popular. Many feel that the eating quality of foods cooked by the sous vide method is comparatively better than that of foods produced by the cook-chill method. By cooking at lower temperatures, less protein denaturing occurs, which gives better texture and yield. The packaging prevents loss of flavour and moisture during cooking, and low oxygen tension within the pack inhibits oxidative changes, which are responsible for developing off-flavours.

7.5.10 Details required for product specifications

After determining the method of cook needed for the product to be produced, all details must be laid out clearly in the product specifications:

- Type of cooking method
- Length of cook
- Temperatures to be achieved

- Cooling methods
- Storage conditions
- Colour and texture
- Life after cook
- Batch traceability
- Photographic standards

7.6 Preparation

7.6.1 Storage

The following temperature conditions should be observed.

Blast freezers -30 °C (when freezing prepared components, or meals)
Holding freezers -18 °C
Dry storage 8-10 °C
Ambient storage 12 °C
Holding chills 0-5 °C

Temperature controls can be either electronic or by hand-held probes, but all records must be kept and a set time specified for the recording of temperatures. Cooked and raw foods must never be kept together. Low-risk and high-risk preparation conditions must be separated to avoid cross-contamination when manufacturing prepared meals. Surfaces used for preparation should, where possible, be jointless, impervious, durable and at the correct working height with a firm base. Stainless steel is the most durable and hygienic material; however, there are many laminated plastics that can be used. All surfaces must be resistant to staining, chemicals, heat, and food acids. To avoid any cross-contamination, each preparation area should have its own colour-coded system for easy recognition, i.e. Yellow; High Risk, Red; Low Risk, Green, Hygiene, etc. This also helps management controls in observation of the rules. Routine maintenance on all equipment is essential as broken or chipped utensils and machinery will cause bacterial problems.

7.6.2 Cooking

When all the appropriate specifications have been set, cooking becomes the next factor in maintaining the quality of the meals to be prepared. Through development and trials, a recipe will be created, and this is then put to the test. Achieving consistent quality and taste will depend on the cooking method required.

Each component will have a process to follow (recipe) describing what is needed for any specific meal to be made.

ɔd of cook: This will depend on batch size, type of cook, texture ,equired and temperatures to be achieved.

b) *Batch size:* This will be based on what is required to attain the quality needed. It could be as small as one batch or a whole day's production. All batches must be clearly documented according to weight (yield), time of production, shelf life and use-by date, and any other information required. This helps in batch traceability in case of rejection and easy accessibility should any product need to be recalled. A positive release system of every batch made is a safeguard against expensive product recall should a non-conforming component find its way to final product.

c) *Type of cook:* This will be determined by the type of meal being produced, i.e. grill, retort, fry, open pan, automated kettles, sous vide marinating before cook, etc.

d) *Texture and viscosity:* Texture of vegetables – i.e. al dente or soft – must be defined in the method of cooking. Viscosity of sauces should also be made clear, to ensure any starch or stabilisers have been incorporated. pH should be defined and acidity levels tested.

e) *Temperatures:* Cooking temperatures should be clearly defined to ensure setting of sauces, and achievement of the desired texture of vegetables, tenderness of meat, etc. Cooling regimes should also be specified to ensure bacterial safety.

The success of the process of cooking selected is judged by taste panel as a final test before release. Standards are supplied for acceptance or rejection, including presentation, flavour and texture, specific size of components within the meal, etc.

7.6.3 Labelling

Throughout production and preparation, all components must be labelled correctly – date of preparation, kill dates, weight, harvest dates, use by, life of components, quality, colour, and adherence to specification. Packaging and labelling of finished product must contain all relevant information, including storage conditions, and recommended cooking time. This information should have been set into the specification during the development process.

7.6.4 Summary of requirements for preparation

- Define designated areas for all food components

- Determine high-risk and low-risk categories
- Ensure that all internal temperatures are achieved at each step of preparation
- All components and product to be chilled or frozen quickly and maintained at correct holding temperature
- No components left out in warm humid conditions
- All equipment used colour coded for easy identification
- All staff trained to specific processes, and all personnel to have achieved Basic Food Hygiene Certificate
- Hygiene schedules
- Pest controls
- Water testing
- Microbiological controls
- Foreign body controls
- Start-up procedures

7.7 Presentation of Product

The product must be assembled in accordance with agreed standards, with regard to the lay-out of any meal, pack, etc. Photographic standards would be useful to ensure that, in the case of a multi-component product, components, e.g. meat, potato, and vegetables (which may have individual compartments), are put in the correct place. On-line quality standards are another way of ensuring that the product is assembled correctly, and that all temperatures have been checked, as well as the life of each component, target weights and ranges. Standards laid down like this would also include metal detection required for that product, declared and T1 rejection weights, and the final product life.

It must be ensured that all meals are microbiologically safe, through lab. sampling, and that they are presented to the colour standards and size of components required. Foreign body contamination through handling must be prevented and all staff must conform to the personal hygiene standards required by law of persons handling food. Compliance with Food Safety Regulations and trading standards weights and measures must be incorporated, and all systems must be recorded, and adequate staff training provided. Where QC is adopted, all aspects of weight control must be recorded, especially where manual assembly of product is required. All equipment that measures or weighs components or product must have calibration certification. Tasting of finished product is another quality standard that can be measured, and this is advisable before despatch. If the manufacturer has the facilities, a taste panel can be put into place, which follows the guidelines of finished eating quality required by the customer. Other measures could be having a batch standard as a sample for measurement against – for example frozen products, dried products. Checks should be in place to ensure that packaging is of the required quality and size (including sleeves, inserts, cartons, or boxes).

7.7.1 Summary of checks to be carried out

- *Start-up procedures – assembly lines:* checks should be carried out before product is assembled; strict controls on meat and vegetarian segregation, and general condition of equipment to be used.
- *Foreign body audits:* to reduce danger to customer and the expense of customer complaints.
- *Glass audit:* inventory of all glass or clear Perspex that may be construed as glass.
- *On-line quality standards:* how the product is assembled and all relevant information for the product – maybe photographic standards (Fig. 7.1).
- *Daily personnel health check:* to ensure safety to the consumer.
- *Weight control checks:* to eliminate waste and to conform to Trading Standard regulations.
- *Scale calibration:* to ensure that all weights are within the range and targets laid out in the specification.
- *Lab. sampling:* for microbiological and chemical safety for the customer.
- *Taste and end of life sampling:* for checking that the product taste is consistent. End of life sampling to ensure that weight and taste are the same after completion of shelf life (Fig. 7.2).
- *Temperature control:* to prevent bacterial activity and spoilage, and ensure correct storage of components.
- *Personnel hygiene check:* to ensure that all personnel follow the correct procedures for hand washing, hair hygiene, protective clothing, etc.
- *Hygiene standards:* set schedules for the cleaning and sterilisation of all machinery, and other equipment used.
- *Engineering standards:* corrective maintenance and work that has been carried out is signed off and checked following major or running repairs.

ON LINE QUALITY STANDARDS

PRODUCT

AREA

ALLOWABLE TOLERANCES FOR WEIGHTS, TEMPERATURES AND LIFE.

COMPONENT	WEIGHT	RANGE	LIFE	TEMP.

Weigh 103 g of chicken fillets into the smaller compartment of the pet tray. Ensure a minimum of 3 chicken fillets per product, ensuring no broken pieces.

Turbo deposit 100 g of lemon & thyme sauce over the chicken. Ensure the chicken is fully covered.

Weigh 203 g of lemon parsley rice and place in larger compartment. Ensure the rice is evenly spread with no clumping.

Ensure there is no rice in the sauce compartment and vice versa.

Seal on pa machine using a clear film. Ensure a firm seal.

Sleeve and code. Price £2.49. Shelf life p+5+1

Metal detect: 2-mm ferrous 2.5-mm non-ferrous.

Check weigh. Declared weight 400 g T1 388 g

Despatch 0-5 °C

NO MEALS, OR COMPONENTS TO BE LEFT ON THE FACTORY FLOOR DURING BREAKS, OR BREAKDOWNS.

ALL COMPONENTS AND FINISHED PRODUCT TO BE CLEARLY LABELLED IN CHILLED STORAGE.

THIS PRODUCT MUST BE WELL PRESENTED WITH NO MESSY EDGES OR FOOD DEBRIS ON CONTAINERS.

IF ANY OF THESE CONDITIONS CANNOT BE MET, CONSULT A TEAM LEADER AND TECHNOLOGIST.

Fig. 7.1. On-line quality standards

PRODUCT QUALITY STANDARDS

Eating Quality

Crispy savoury pastry shell. Light golden brown in colour when reheated.
Savoury mince filling, with a strong beef taste.
Creamy mashed potato with a mild cheese and onion flavour.

Visual Appearance

Light brown pastry case.
Topped with cheese and onion mashed potato.
Mince may be slightly evident around edge of pastry case.
Mashed potato to fully cover mince fill – although some small patches of mince may be visible.
Mashed potato centred on top of mince fill.

Once Cooked

Pastry case will turn a darker golden brown colour.
Cheese and onion mash may turn golden brown on peals of potato.
Mince may slightly boil up around edge of pastry case – although no boil-outs should be visible.

Pack Presentation

X 12 Mini Cottage Pies per pack.
No broken. Cracked pastry shells to be used.
Mashed potato centred on top of mince fill.
Potato piped through star shaped nozzle giving a pattern to the potato.
Mince may be slightly evident around edge of pastry case.

Photographs should be used where appropriate, to further define visual standards.

Fig. 7.2. Presentation and eating qualities

7.8 Despatch

All products must be at the correct temperature, coded and priced and in the correct packaging. Chilled product should be held for despatch at 0-5 °C, and frozen product at -18 °C; ambient conditions are satisfactory for dried products. Vehicles transporting goods should be monitored and records kept ensuring that each vehicle is running at the correct temperature. Vehicles should be in good condition, clean and odour-free. A relevant breakdown procedure should be in place, which should include storage of product so that, in the case of a breakdown, especially in the case of chilled or frozen products, temperature is not compromised. Final checks should be carried out to evaluate the numbers of products for despatch, and to ensure that final destination for delivery is clear and precise. All meals must be free from contamination and therefore not injurious to public health.

7.8.1 Summary of checks for despatch of product

- Despatch vehicle inspection
- Despatch notice
- Temperature checks
- Foreign body checks
- Glass audit
- Cleaning schedule
- Breakdown procedure

7.9 Starches and Stabilisers

Starches and stabilisers are used to enhance presentation and shelf life; they can also contribute to the structure of processed foods. They are versatile and have many uses, the most common food starches being maize, potato, wheat, tapioca and rice. There are many speciality starches that provide properties that would be desired in all types of food product, including a range of canned foods; chilled, frozen, microwaveable meals; dry mixes; and snacks. The use of speciality starches has many benefits; they can replace expensive ingredients, and increase efficiency, stability, and final quality, therefore ensuring consistent end product for customer satisfaction. Choosing starches and stabilisers depends on the type of meal to be prepared and this is evaluated at the development stage and incorporated into the specification for the product to be produced.

Some typical uses and common properties of common starches are shown in Table 7.II.

There are many uses for the addition of starches and stabilisers and this should all be considered when seeking the correct application for meals that need to be produced. It would be entirely a matter of balancing the cost and the quality required in the end product.

There are two types of chemical modification performed on starches – cross-linking and stabilisation.

With cross-linking, the hydrogen bond is removed by the use of chemicals, and a 1% change increases the robustness of the starch granule. Where fewer chemicals are used in the cross-linked starches, this would be suitable for use where lower temperatures are required.

When considering the use of cross-linked starches for processing, time, temperature, and shear (mixing) must be considered. Acidity (pH), sugar, and enzymes must also be taken into account. The lower the pH, the more hydrogen bonds are broken.

TABLE 7.II
Types of starch

Type of starch	Properties	Uses
Potato starch	Initial gelatinisation temperature (IGT) low (58 °C). Clear paste formed. Little tendency to gel; neutral in flavour.	Used to thicken soups, which would curdle at high temperatures.
Tapioca	Low IGT (52 °C). Produces an exceptionally clear paste.	The liquor from the cooked starch is used to thicken consommé. Pearl tapioca is used for puddings. Flake tapioca is used for garnishing.
Rice (crème de riz)	IGT higher (68 °C). Clear pastes are formed more quickly than with potato starch. The gels are opaque and very tender.	The starch is used for thickening soups. Short-grain (Carolina rice) is used for pudding, long-grain rice in savoury dishes.
Cornflour	IGT 62 °C. Forms cloudy pastes. Gels are very stiff but tend to retrograde, particularly when frozen and thawed	Thickening sauce. Disadvantage – lumps form easily; may crack if used for glazing.
Arrowroot	Forms clear pastes.	Thickening lemon sauce (clear). Glaze for fruit flans
Waxy rice flour	Natural flour with high freeze-thaw stability.	White sauces and starch-thickened puddings in cook-freeze operation.

In regard to stabilisation, this process affects textural stability, resists retrogradation, improves freeze/thaw stability and increases shelf life. Stabilisers block amyloses from binding together.

7.9.1 Sugar

Sugar needs water and takes the water from the starch, so the starch takes longer to cook. The greater the amount of sugar in a product, the more delicate the gel formed. Sugar prevents water from being bound to the starch chain, and a "sticky syrup" is formed within the gel. The alternative would be to cook starches, and stabilisers are also used to enhance presentation and shelf life.

7.9.2 *Acid*

Acids can break the starch chains, so the gel process becomes thinner. When considering the addition of, e.g., vinegar or lemon juice, it would be appropriate to add these components after the thickening process.

7.9.3 *Fat*

Fat gives flavour and texture to sauces, soups, etc., and the main function is to enable the starch granules to suspend individually, which prevents lumps from forming in hot liquid. When higher amounts of fat are present, the fat coats the starch granule and stops water from being absorbed into the starch granule; this will increase the cooking time.

7.9.4 *Proteins*

Flours used as thickeners behave differently from starches. Cornstarch used for sauces and gels reacts differently from cornflour. The reason is that the protein in flours that are added to dishes, i.e. in the form of egg, meat juices, milk or gelatin, modify the behaviour of starches present quite considerably. Proteins that are dry absorb substantial amounts of water, so, when considering, for example, constituents for a batter, wheat flour contains more protein than wheat starch. Proteins improve freeze-thaw stability of starch pastes as they help bind water inside the gels.

7.9.5 *Retrogradation*

Changes occur when starch gel is stored; this causes the starch to contract and therefore squeeze out some of the water that is normally held inside. When this occurs, the gel has an opaque appearance and appears spongy; this causes serious problems when making starch-thickened dishes, during the cook-freeze process. To overcome this, consideration must be given to the type of starch to be used. Natural starches, e.g. waxy rice flour, would eliminate this problem, although, as more and more research goes on into modified starches, there are now even better alternatives available.

7.9.6 *Enzymes*

Amylase breaks O-bonds of amylose and then degrades the rest of the starch; however, enzymes do not degrade unhydrated starch granules.

7.9.7 Heat-modified starch

Heat-modified rather than chemically modified starch produces a smooth, more natural taste and has short texture. It does not mask flavours and can be used in organic foods; the usual ratio would need to be 5-10% in product, benefits being:

- Stable viscosity
- Shear- and pH-tolerant
- Stable end product
- Heightened flavour

7.9.8 Instant starches

Pregelatinised and cold-water swelling.

7.9.9 Ultra starches

These are resistant starches, keeping the granules whole.

7.10 Colour Standards

Determining the colour of the components for the product being produced is an essential part of the overall quality. If the meal looks colourful and freshly cooked, then it will be also be appealing to the customer. For instance, a ready-made meal with carrots and peas would not look appetising were the carrots very pale or the peas slightly off-colour. Setting colour standards for each component to be used before and after cook should help in ensuring that the look of the meal is consistent. There are several ways of controlling colour standards.

Supplier specification should take into account what that supplier is capable of producing. Soils differ in the UK, affecting the colour; this would also apply to imported fruit and vegetables. Buyers must inspect and approve acceptable colour standards at this point.

7.10.1 Colour fans

These are produced by the British Horticultural Society and contain colour fans of every different hue, found in all plants and vegetables. When monitoring the colour standard, a reference to a fan number will also give allowable colour either side of the optimum and is useful in calibrating what the eye perceives. An example could be 'Spring Cabbage', the colour being a rich dark green, but, depending on the season and the elements, this may vary a little. Here standards can be set to allow for these subtle changes and would ensure that seasonal variation did not affect the look of the final component. This principle can be set for all components to ensure that colour standards are maintained. The application for materials after cooking can also follow the same principle and this also will depend on the length of cook, and how the final colour will appear after reheating by the consumer.

7.10.2 Photographic colour standards

A series of photographs can be taken for control against what is acceptable and what is not. This could be incorporated on delivery and after each stage of preparation and would probably be most efficient within a factory situation. Colour fans used throughout production would be messy and time-consuming. Photographs could be laminated and placed in appropriate situations at every step of production, so that all personnel could check against them. All organoleptic standards must be set into the product specification, and within those standards colour and texture must be a control point. Examples: i) Pale creamy sauce with flecks of parsley: How pale is the colour cream? Is the parsley bright or dull? Does the colour change before and after cook? ii) Rich dark onion gravy: Is it almost black? Is it caramel? Do the onions change colour in cooking? All these colour standards could be shown with colour photographs and the expectation of the colour throughout processing. Fish such as salmon could be measured against the Torré scale colour chart, fried components or product showing the depth of colour needed.

When setting colour standards, natural north light is the best light for seeing the true colour. However, this is not really practical, and other methods can be employed. Artificial lighting or direct sunlight is not advisable as these can enhance or detract from the true colour. If the standards cannot be met by natural light, then artificial daylight bulbs are available (D 65); this bulb would give the best standard, if used consistently.

7.11 Measuring Quality

7.11.1 Quality management systems

Quality systems measure performance throughout the whole of production. Traditionally, manufacturers have operated systems that rely on checking an inspection to measure conformance to requirements. Often, defects were not discovered until manufacture was at an advanced stage, resulting in cost, waste and delays; sometimes, defects were not recognised at all and therefore reduced profit. Processes have become more complex and costly, and safety is crucial to a sound customer base. Many large purchasers now insist that their suppliers do more than test and inspect a product before delivery. They require that activities be organised in such a way that effective quality management is implemented and maintained through the whole process, from initial enquiry to final delivery. Many customers now insist on proof that a quality system is in place, operating effectively and being systematically reviewed before placing orders. In this way, they are able to establish a level of confidence in the supplier. There are many systems that may be adopted.

7.11.2 Quality assurance systems

The ISO 9000 series of standards incorporates a third party independent audit for recognition, and involves first party internal audits and second party customer audits, to ensure that all processes conform to what is required. Other organisations include the British Retail Consortium EFSIS.

7.11.3 Total quality management

This is an assessment system that is management-led. This system relies on quality assessments internally and, if the business required, could apply for the Baldridge Award and European Foundation Quality Management (EFQM).

7.11.4 Quality control

This system takes samples and measures against specification and enables reaction to non-conformance quickly. Line operatives should be given training against the quality standards required, but quality controllers should carry out checks at regular intervals throughout production. Quality control would also incorporate all other aspects of food safety, i.e., glass audits, metal detection checks, water sampling, foreign body audits, product analysis, weight controls, coding and pricing, and temperature controls, corrective actions, process controls, hygiene schedules, pest control, product segregation.

7.11.5 Setting quality standards

In setting the standards required for quality, all personnel must be trained to understand quality, from management to shop floor. This training should set standards and procedures to which each department (Engineering, Technical, Preparation, Production, and Distribution) could be trained against and would form part of the HACCP plan, so that hazards and control points can be audited to determine any reassessments that might need to be taken. Each process must have a defined structure to eliminate the possibility of contamination whether it be microbiological, physical or chemical. Training all personnel in every department will determine quality through each process and pinpoint areas of high risk that could detract from the end result. Through consultation and implementation of all processes of manufacture, quality can be achieved. There are several avenues of measuring quality and it would depend on the scope of manufacture.

7.11.6 Process approach to quality management

A process approach to quality encourages ownership of every aspect of manufacture. Any activity that is part of the process, either receiving or sending out materials or product, must have an inter-linked system that identifies and manages the several parts required to achieve safety and quality. No matter how large or small the manufacturer, a sound system must also have relevant documentation. It must include defined procedures for all processes, be documented and available for all users be used, and be understood by all, so that they know what is required of them. A three-level approach will integrate all that is required for every process to be carried out.

Level one – Quality Manual. Incorporated into this should be the policies of the company and the standards that it can achieve. Management involvement in policies will show their commitment to quality.

Level two – Procedures Manual. These documents usually form the bulk of the QMS; they describe how the policy objectives are met in practice and how processes are controlled. They describe the processes and the controls but do not usually go into detail; it is usually what, when and who, but the final "how" is left to the work instructions.

Level three – Work Instructions. Detailed instructions are given on how to complete a task, e.g. a procedure might mention that a particular component is this shape – the accompanying work instruction gives details on how to achieve this.

Both procedures and work instructions are documents, which, although not read every day are solid training aids, especially for new employees and those new to their role. Deciding the level of detail required in work instructions can often be difficult and it is usually found to vary with the skill level of the user. The presentation of work instructions is also important; they should be such that the user will want to refer to them when in doubt. Movement has been made to a more visual approach using illustrations, diagrams and colour photography; they are more attractive than wordy documents. Remember that not all employees will learn at the same rate and therefore this type of instruction could be invaluable.

Each level of documentation becomes more detailed and generally applies to fewer people within the business; i.e. work instructions are more detailed than procedures, which are in turn more detailed than policies.

If the criteria below can be achieved, then the product should be of consistent quality.

- All personnel understanding quality.
- Individual's commitment.
- Manufacturing policy.
- Planning.
- Establishing quality.
- Customer satisfaction.
- Cost.
- Is it quality-consistent? benchmarking.
- All department input through HACCP.
- Training and re-assessment.
- Controls documented and evaluated.
- Effectiveness.

7.11.7 Requirements

- Identify all processes needed to ensure quality.
- Determine the sequence and inter-linking of these processes
- Ensure that specifications and methods used are effective and controlled.
- Ensure that all information to fulfill the processes is available and monitored.
- Analyse, measure and monitor to implement any actions required, to achieve the end result and look for continuous improvement.

7.11.8 Quality principles

Customers: Every business relies on its customers and, through innovation and understanding of customer needs, the measurement of a quality system is vital. Customer complaints will also show how well or how badly the product is performing. If there are inadequate controls, customer loyalty will go.

Leadership: With good leadership giving direction and their full commitment to quality, all levels are involved in an atmosphere where they feel involved.

Involvement of people: Everyone must be involved in the quality of production, with the correct training required, so they can use these abilities to produce the quality expected by the customer.

Approaching the process: Where processes are efficiently managed throughout the manufacturing of product, waste and costly errors should be eliminated. Understanding and identifying change that may affect the final outcome will save costs incurred by product returns or contamination.

Management review: There should be ownership and commitment by management to provide the driving force to the company's commitment to quality.

Continuous improvement: Constant monitoring and audits of the systems in place will ensure that controls are working. Through this, even more efficiencies may be achieved, which in turn saves money and increases customer satisfaction.

Sound factual approach: Ensure that the improvements are logical and effective; it would be no use coming up with an improvement that may cost the company money and is not achievable.

Supplier relationship: This will benefit both parties and develops trust.

Adopt best practice: A committed health and safety policy should be adopted and commitment given to the laws governing the manufacture and sale of food and all its amendments.

Document controls: Ensure that any changes, such as additions or withdrawals to the system, are controlled. This prevents out-of-date actions or alterations being left in the system, which in turn could put the system of control at risk.

7.12 Summary

Quality is what a product depends on, be it a quick snack or a gourmet meal. With so many meals available, to find a market place, a company's product is even more reliant upon, reliability, trust and the knowledge that what is eaten is safe for consumption. Customer loyalty can only be achieved by a sound manufacturing basis, which is managed and efficient.

By incorporating a workable and controlled quality system, whether it is for large manufacture or a small teashop, the principles must always be the same.

8. CHOOSING THE PACKAGING

Anne and Henry Emblem

8.1 Introduction

Without packaging, many of the exciting developments we have seen and continue to see in ready meal technology would not be possible. This chapter addresses the fundamental requirements of packaging in this market, reviews the main packaging types used, and considers the factors to be taken into account when selecting packaging materials and formats.

8.2 The Role of Packaging

In its most basic role, packaging contributes to the extension of the shelf life of food products, the extent of that contribution being determined by the requirements of the product and the preservation method used. For example, where products are preserved by means of heat treatment to destroy the harmful microorganisms, the packaging must prevent subsequent ingress of such organisms; where modified-atmosphere techniques are used, the packaging is required to maintain the required gas composition within the pack. This is commonly referred to as the preservation role of packaging and is a key consideration for food products such as ready meals, where one important question usually asked is how good a barrier is the pack to the identified spoilage mechanism. Sought-after properties include moisture, gas and light barrier, both in the chosen packaging materials and in the construction of the finished pack format, i.e. in the way in which the pack is made up and sealed. Seal integrity, in particular, is usually of critical importance. Often, the packaging alone is not sufficient to provide the required shelf life and must work in conjunction with specific storage conditions, for example in chilled and frozen meals. Here the main preservation mechanism is the use of reduced temperatures to slow down microbial spoilage, and prevent deterioration during the life of the product.

Ready meals also require protection against physical damage to prevent undesirable effects such as breakage of delicate pastry, or squashing of vegetables, and packaging can be constructed to provide the required level of protection for the life cycle of the product, from the end of the packaging line to its consumption by the consumer. Throughout this life cycle just some of the potentially adverse conditions encountered include mechanical hazards, vibration, compression, and environmental hazards (temperature and humidity changes).

One hazard requiring particular attention is the human one of tampering, whether it be the relatively innocent opening of a pack to see what it looks like or perhaps to taste its contents, or the more sinister deliberate contamination. Tamper-evident features need to be considered as part of the pack design, including some visible means of identifying tampering attempts. Some pack types may be regarded as inherently tamper-evident, e.g. heat-sealed sachets. Others are designed with additional features incorporated into the closure system – for example, the use of a locking ring on a plastic tub, where a small tab of plastic must be broken away before the lid can be removed. While most current tamper-evident features are concentrated on the pack closure as being the usual means of gaining access to the product, it is worth remembering that a serious tamperer is unlikely to be constrained by such convention, and consideration should be given at the pack design stage to all possible points of entry to the product. Of course, it will not be possible to totally stop the resolute tamperer, intent on harm, and for this reason 'tamper-evident' and not 'tamper-proof' packaging is the realistic objective. To be effective, tamper-evident features must be obvious to the consumer and easily recognisable when breached and this may mean that a consumer education programme needs to be considered. This can be done by means of advertising campaigns and on-pack information.

Packaging's role of containment is especially relevant for ready meals, not just in terms of preventing leakage but in bringing together a number of separate components needed for one meal, e.g. a curried dish with cooked rice and accompaniments such as chutney and dried fruits. Packaging can be designed to bring the component parts of such a meal together, but kept separate until required. This may necessitate different packaging materials to meet different barrier requirements and different modes of preparation, with the over-riding need to deliver all parts intact and in good condition.

Inherent in the development and success of ready meal technology is the need to meet the consumer's demand for convenience, which has been driven by a reduction in culinary skills, and increased foreign travel (see Chapter 1).

Two important convenience features on the consumer's list of expectations for all products are pack openability and, if relevant, resealability. Good packaging design takes account of the needs of the intended consumer and the conditions under which the pack is likely to be opened, and provides safe and easy access to the product. Opening a ready meal pack should be intuitive and should not require complex instructions, or special opening implements. It should present no threat to the user and result in no loss of product through spillage. Packaging has the opportunity to meet all of these requirements.

Another important contribution to the acceptance and convenience of ready meals for the consumer is the presentation of clear, easy-to-understand instructions. This role of providing a means of giving the consumer information can only be met by the packaging, which must be printed with instructions such as how to store, prepare, cook and use the product. Graphics depicting serving suggestions provide an immediate source of information – or aspiration – in store, but once the purchase has been made and taken home, the would-be 'cook' is all alone with the packed product, usually with no other source of help than what is printed on the pack. As part of both the functional and graphic design of the pack, consideration needs to be given to how much information will be required and how best to present it. Instructions should be easy to locate amongst other information printed on the pack and should preferably be read when the pack is the correct way up. Pictorial instructions tend to work better than complex written text and type matter should clearly contrast with background colours and use a simple type face. Many brand owners have adopted a 'house' style, placing information in boxed sections and using consistent colour coding and, where possible, location, for different types of information, e.g. usage, nutritional data, warning statements, contact and 'customer care' details.

Packaging in today's retail environment is a selling tool. To 'win' in the selection process, the product must first of all be noticed; it must stand out, catch the shopper's attention and be quickly recognised for what it is. It must then meet whatever the particular need is at that moment, e.g. 'quick and easy', 'exotic', etc., and it must offer some assurance that it will deliver its promise, commonly given by its brand image. Colour, especially, plays an important role in attracting attention and gaining immediate recognition of the product.

Thus, packaging has a number of different roles to play, both technical and aesthetic, and each of these roles must be evaluated and understood at the packaging design stage. In addition, there are two factors that must always be considered alongside what has been stated so far, and these are economics and environmental aspects.

Packaging costs must be in line with the position of the product and, while no one wants to spend money on packaging unnecessarily, it would be foolish to cut costs to the point where the pack's performance is compromised. This applies just as much to the selling function of the pack as it does to the protection and preservation functions; if the graphic design of the pack does not attract the attention of and appeal to the target market, it will not succeed in that marketplace. With regard to environmental aspects, all packs placed on the market in countries of the European Community must comply with Directive EC 94/62 on Packaging and

Packaging Waste. Some of the implications of this are discussed briefly in section 8.7.

8.3 A Short History of Ready Meal Packaging

Ready meals began in the early 1800s with the development of the process of heating food in a hermetically sealed container, as a means of long-term preservation. The first containers used were wide-mouthed glass jars, and in 1810 the tin-plated can with its soldered seams was developed. This combined development of food processing and packaging, said to be brought about by Napoleon I, who demanded wholesome rations for his far-flung armies, is the forerunner of today's extensive canning industry. Emphasis is still on the preservation role of the packaging, as was shown in the 1960s with the move from 3-piece to 2-piece cans to reduce the number of potential leakage points. Modern refinements such as the full-aperture ring-pull end, which has now been developed to its third generation design, are helping to address consumer problems of opening the can and removing the product, and thus the food can is becoming more convenient to use, although at the same time it retains its traditional image.

One of the disadvantages of the canning process is that the heat required to penetrate the can and the food in order to guarantee commercial sterility also brings about changes to the taste and texture of the product. The development of the retort pouch in the 1970s was an attempt to address this. By filling and sealing the food in a slim multi-layer flexible pouch with a large surface area, the time required for heat to penetrate the product is vastly reduced. However, the shape and structure of the flexible pouch presented several problems, such as the difficulty in displaying it neatly on shelf and its susceptibility to physical damage, both of which were addressed by packing the pouches into printed cartons, thus further increasing cost. Also, if the product was reheated in the pouch, trying to open a hot and unwieldy structure presented problems. Thus, after an initial flurry of marketing activity and consumer interest, pouches all but disappeared except for military rations, where their low weight was a significant advantage when out on manoeuvres. However, they are now enjoying a revival, and this is covered later in this chapter.

Aluminium foil containers first appeared in the 1950s and were the first containers used for 'convenience' foods, such as the American-inspired frozen TV dinner and the Chinese and Indian ready-to-eat 'take-away' meal. The handy tray format offered better presentation than either the can or the pouch, reduced weight versus the can, and gave the consumer the convenience of being able to reheat the food quickly in the tray and even eat directly from it. These advantages continue to apply today and account for the wide usage of this type of pack not only in the retail sector but also in catering, both in bulk supply and for uses such as airline meals. Foil containers are discussed further in the next section.

The growth in domestic ownership of refrigerators and freezers throughout the 1960s and 1970s developed alongside a greater use of chilling and freezing as alternative methods of commercial food preservation, and consequently a greater interest in and market for ready-prepared foods. Instead of relying primarily on heat processing to prolong shelf life, food manufacturers could now offer an attractive range of chilled and frozen meal dishes and accompaniments. The tray style of packaging format lent itself well to these products, offering convenience and a shape and geometry that allowed for fast cooling and heating. In moving away from the cylindrical shape of the can, it also brought new opportunities and challenges for on-shelf presentation. Developments of the food tray continued throughout the 1970s and 1980s, firstly using ovenable board and then, with the commercial availability of polyethylene terephthalate (PET) for packaging, using plastic trays that could be heated in a conventional oven. The development of the domestic microwave oven in the 1970s and its widespread home ownership in the 1980s and 1990s further stimulated consumer demand for ready meals and brought a requirement for microwave-stable packaging.

8.4 Current Packaging Types

This section reviews packaging currently used in a wide range of ready meal products.

8.4.1 Aluminium foil containers

There are two main types of aluminium foil container – wrinkle-wall and smooth-wall – and both are used in the ready meals sector. They are made from reels of aluminium and are delivered in stacks to the packer/filler.

In the wrinkle-wall process, the folds contribute significantly to the strength of the container, making it particularly useful for producing deep containers. Wrinkle-wall containers are produced in a wide range of shapes and sizes, shallow and deep containers, including those with multi-compartments for product segregation, e.g. meat and vegetables. Pies, quiches, flans and pizzas lend themselves best to shallow, round dishes, which are then placed into printed cartons, in some cases wrapped first in film bags. Most other products in the ready meals sector that use wrinkle-wall containers have adopted rectangular or square or, sometimes, oval shapes, and one of the most common methods of closure is by the use of a board lid secured in place by folding down the flange of the container. This type of closure is not liquid-tight and, dependent on the product consistency, instructions to keep the container upright may be required to avoid leakage.

Wrinkle-wall containers with a heat-sealable rim are available, under the trade name Plage Lisse™, and these allow a liquid-tight (but not a gas-tight) closure (1).

Smooth-wall containers are stamped and drawn – a process that allows the flange area to be produced with a high level of accuracy, flatness and smoothness, allowing the container to be securely closed by heat sealing. There are two main variants of smooth-wall containers – coated and uncoated. Coated containers have been available for many years and are used for pet foods, snacks such as pâtés and prepared foods such as fish dishes and pasta. They are closed with a lacquered foil or laminate lid, which bonds to the internal coating of the container and forms a gas- and liquid-tight hermetic seal, which resists heat processing and provides a long shelf life at ambient temperatures.

A more recent development is the use of uncoated smooth-wall containers, which are sealed with a film lid. A mechanical bond is formed between the film lid and the uncoated foil, giving a liquid-tight seal that dispenses with the need to keep the pack upright, allowing it to be displayed on its side if desired. Perhaps of more significance for food preservation is the fact that it also gives a gas-tight seal and can thus be used in combination with the modified-atmosphere-packaging (MAP) process to further extend shelf life. Uncoated smooth-wall containers with film lids are being used for a variety of products, such as chilled meat dishes, pasta in sauce, marinated meats for the barbecue and roasted vegetables. Lidding films are available in polyethylene terephthalate (PET) with and without an ethylene vinyl acetate (EVA) sealing layer, which lowers the sealing temperature from 170-200 °C to 140-160 °C and in Surlyn® coated nylon, which has a sealing temperature range of 140-180 °C. The films can be designed to be anti-fogging, allowing good product visibility, and to be easy-peel (2).

Foil containers provide excellent barrier to light, moisture gain or loss, odour pick-up and flavour loss, subject, of course, to the integrity of the closure. Foil is regarded as inert and does not support microorganism growth. Containers can be internally coated for extra resistance to highly acidic foods and externally lacquered or printed for decoration, simple branding and easy product differentiation. Foil is an excellent conductor of heat, making it highly suitable for both chilled and frozen meals, which can be readily cooked or reheated in the original container and the used pack easily disposed of, thus contributing to consumer convenience. With special precautions, aluminium foil containers can also be used in the microwave oven (3), although it must be said that food manufacturers tend to err on the side of caution here and give instructions that the product should be emptied into a microwave-safe container.

While strength characteristics can be designed into foil containers by the correct choice of alloy and gauge of aluminium, as well as shape, folds and embossing, they do remain susceptible to deformation during handling in the supply chain. Also, they do not offer an ideal surface on which to present detailed graphic design to contribute to the selling function of the pack while on display, and there is limited flat space for important information such as product description, instructions and ingredients. Thus, whilst a few, mainly 'budget-brand' products are distributed without any further primary packaging, the majority have an additional component in the form of a printed board carton or sleeve, and these are reviewed later in this section.

8.4.2 Ovenable board trays

Developments in the 1970s allowed the commercial introduction of food containers made from ovenable board, to meet the growing demand for microwaveable meals that could be conveniently reheated in the original container. A pack that could also withstand heating in a conventional oven would provide even greater convenience as the consumer would not be faced with the potential confusion that some containers are suitable only for one heating method and some only for another. Hence, what is now sometimes called the dual-ovenable board tray was developed and it is this type of tray that is discussed here.

The challenge was to impart the combined performance properties of grease resistance, liquid hold-out and heat resistance to withstand both microwave and conventional oven temperatures, into a paperboard construction. The board is made from high-quality kraft sulfate pulp, usually bleached white and coated with a PET film layer for the inside of the tray. The bleached kraft outer surface provides an excellent printing medium and the PET inner layer provides product resistance, heat resistance and a sealable surface at the flange and corners, plus the required level of moisture and gas barrier properties for the product.

Two types of container are currently in use. The one that appears to be most prevalent at the moment is made by pressing, and is available in round, square, oval and rectangular shapes, including multi-compartments. This type of container can be closed by means of a domed lid or, if a liquid-tight pack is required, a heat-sealable and peelable PET film or coated board lid is available, which allows the pack to be displayed on its side. The finished pack is generally not gas-tight and thus not suitable for use in modified-atmosphere packaging. The second type, seen in use mainly for frozen meals, is shaped not by pressing but by folding flat blanks of printed, heat-seal-coated board at the corners, to give a neat, rectangular or similar shape. The lid is a fully printed coated board, heat-sealed in place.

Ovenable board trays are used for both chilled and frozen meals and, although their use has been static, it is expected to grow as board manufacturers develop materials and processes to improve barrier properties. Board trays are fairly robust in terms of withstanding the physical hazards of distribution and handling in store, and the fact that both the container and the film or board lid can be fully printed means that the use of an outer carton or sleeve may not be necessary, although they are currently still widely used. There is thus the potential to reduce the overall amount of packaging used for a product, although of course this must always be thoroughly tested during development to ensure that the packs withstand the rigours of handling in the supply chain and that unacceptable damage, especially to the seal area, does not occur.

8.4.3 Plastic trays

The use of plastic trays in ready meals is widespread and, for the sake of clarity when discussing packaging, the application is often segregated into two distinct categories. The chilled and ready-to-eat sector, where no cooking or reheating is needed, is outside the scope of this book; the other is the range of both chilled and frozen meals that require either cooking or reheating by the consumer. This segregation is made because of the different performance properties required of the packaging materials used. In both cases, the trays are produced by thermoforming and this can be done in line with filling the product and sealing a top web of film lidding in place, or trays and lids can be purchased already formed, this option being more appropriate to small-scale production.

The plastic trays used for chilled and frozen meals that are cooked or reheated by the consumer have to meet a different set of requirements, the most obvious difference being that, for maximum convenience in use, the packaging has to withstand the heating process demanded by the product. There are some exceptions to this – for example, cooked and chilled chicken pieces that are intended to be eaten either cold or hot are not necessarily supplied in an ovenable pack and instructions to transfer the product to a suitable tray for reheating are provided. Also, fresh pasta that has to be decanted into a pan of boiling water to cook does not require a heat-resistant pack, and a PVC tray with a heat-sealed PVC/LDPE lid is used quite satisfactorily.

However, most products in this sector are cooked in the tray at temperatures in the range of 180 to 250 °C and for these PVC would be totally unsuitable, as would PP and PS. Dependent on grade, PVC has a maximum use temperature of about 95 °C, PP of about 120 °C (thus suitable for boilable and microwave applications) and PS of about 75 °C. The material with the required level of heat resistance is CPET or polyethylene terephthalate in its crystalline form. The familiar highly transparent PET used for carbonated drinks bottles is the amorphous form (APET), in which the molecular arrangement is random. Highly ordered molecular structures are said to be crystalline and, compared with amorphous structures, crystalline materials are more rigid, have a higher melting point and are more opaque. These properties make CPET an ideal material for ovenable trays and account for its widespread use in these applications.

The trays are made by thermoforming cast sheet materials, which can be single-layer CPET or coextruded structures with a layer of APET on the inside of the tray, to improve impact strength and seal performance. Both types are opaque and available in various colours, such as white and cream, with dark colours such as black and brown being increasingly used, especially in the more exotic product ranges such as Indian and Chinese foods. They are mostly heat-sealed with film lids, which are usually PET and can therefore withstand the heating process. The lidding film can be transparent or opaque and provide a liquid- and gas-tight seal suitable for modified-atmosphere packaging. Mostly, the film lids have to be perforated by the consumer prior to placing the pack in the oven, to allow steam to escape, although there is a double-lid system available, which has a pre-perforated lid sealed to the top of the tray and a second lid that is peeled off before cooking. In both cases, the film that has to be removed after cooking should be easy to peel and should come away cleanly from the tray, to limit the extent to which the consumer has to handle the very hot film.

CPET trays are suitable for frozen foods, where they can be taken straight from the freezer to the oven, and for chilled foods, where the use of modified-atmosphere packaging allows extended shelf life with minimal use of artificial preservatives. The range of shapes and sizes available is now extensive, from the familiar shallow rectangular tray to deep bowl shapes, ovals and hexagonal packs, all of which offer good potential for different product positioning. However, the current widespread use of a printed board sleeve around the tray tends to regularise the on-shelf appearance, and the shape of the tray may not be immediately obvious. This sleeve provides both graphics and text to meet the selling and information functions of the pack, as well as physical protection of the sealed tray, although, as the trays are fairly robust, the added protection offered by the board sleeve may not be necessary. If this is proved to be the case (by means of a programme of handling and storage trials), printing the lidding film or applying a label to the lid may allow the sleeve to be dispensed with altogether, thus reducing the overall amount of packaging used.

8.4.4 Plastic pots

Plastic pots (or tubs) refer to the pack format used for wet soups and sauces, which consists of a rigid or semi-rigid container and lid, and to the type of pack used for dry snack meals that are reconstituted by adding hot water. These dry products are commonly packed in a plastic pot and sealed with a peelable film or foil lid. The pots are produced by injection moulding or thermoforming, the former providing a more even wall thickness and greater accuracy of dimensions, although generally at a higher initial tool cost.

In the soups and sauces sector, there are short shelf life chilled and long shelf life ambient products, and the foremost requirements of the consumer for both types are ease of opening and ability to heat the product quickly in its original container. As already stated, tamper evidence is an essential consideration here and the tamper-evident method used should be balanced with ease of opening. In one widely used pack for chilled products, produced by injection moulding of both pot and lid, tamper evidence is achieved by a locking ring on the snap-on lid. There is a tear-off plastic tab, which has to be removed before the lid can be taken off, and removal of this plastic tab may present some difficulties. Screw-threaded pots and lids without tamper evidence are also to be found.

The widespread use of polypropylene for these packs makes the product microwaveable (though not suitable for conventional oven heating) without having to decant it into another container. The lid is removed and then rested loosely on the top of the pot, thus allowing steam to escape. The container can be reclosed using the snap-on lid, and this provides a secure way of storing any unused product. Although PP can now be produced in a highly transparent form by the addition of nucleating agents, in these applications the natural translucency of the material is not a disadvantage and many pots and lids are made in the translucent form. The appearance of the product itself is generally not a major contributor to the selling function and some products use labels on both the pot and the lid, some giving almost total coverage of the pack. Graphic illustrations, rather than visibility of the contents, are used to depict the product either as the ingredients in their natural state or as a serving suggestion, and the remainder of the label area is devoted to the large amount of information required for the consumer.

For this category, the packaging makes only a limited contribution to the preservation of the products and it is the chilled storage and distribution conditions that provide the essential element in maintaining even their short shelf life. For long-life storage at ambient temperature, the packaging barrier requirements are much more demanding and the oxygen barrier of PP alone would be inadequate to provide the required shelf life. Ethylene vinyl alcohol (EVOH) is known for its very high oxygen-barrier properties, and, by incorporating this material into a multi-layer coextrusion, a significant improvement in storage performance can be achieved. H.J. Heinz Company Limited has recently launched a range of Barrier Plus packs made by Huhtamaki, in which a six-layer coextrusion, including EVOH, is thermoformed into pots. The filled containers are heat-sealed with a foil laminate diaphragm lid and retorted to destroy damaging microorganisms, and they then have a shelf life of up to one year at ambient temperatures. One disadvantage of EVOH is its reduction in oxygen-barrier performance in the presence of moisture. By incorporating an oxygen scavenger in the multi-layer structure, Barrier Plus overcomes this problem and the finished pack has both active and passive barrier performance.

The following description of the principles of Barrier Plus is quoted with permission of Packaging News (4).

> 'As humidity levels rise during retorting and the EVOH layer's effectiveness as an oxygen barrier falls, the oxygen scavenging layer begins working, not only preventing oxygen's ingress from outside, but also gathering up residual oxygen within the pot. This occurs for a period of 59 days from retorting, after which humidity has dropped to a negligible level, and the EVOH resumes its normal role'.

This is an exciting development in barrier technology and one that can be expected to find more applications in the ready meals sector. A snap-on PP lid covers the heat-sealed foil laminate diaphragm lid and provides both protection against physical damage during storage and distribution and a flat surface for decoration to enhance branding. The walls of the pot can also be printed, and careful design will allow the packs to be displayed both stacked flat and on edge, and still maintain good visibility and impact to attract the consumer's attention. To use, the foil laminate lid is easily peeled off and the pot is placed in the microwave. The shape of the tub makes it appropriate for direct eating from the pack if desired, thus increasing consumer convenience.

Packaging for the dry snacks sector also has to meet consumer needs and expectations in terms of easy opening and fast heating, and in addition must be easy and safe to hold and eat from, as these products are aimed at the 'eat-on-the-run' market. Peelable lids are widely used and, provided the pull-tab available is sufficient to gain a good grip, and that the heat-sealing operation has been controlled so that the correct degree of peel is achieved, these generally work well. As the products are reconstituted using boiling water, the pot must be able to withstand this and hence PS, PVC and LDPE are not suitable and PP is widely used. The product is meant to be eaten directly from the pot, which therefore must not be too hot to the touch. It should also be of a suitable shape and width to depth ratio, with no large undercuts, so that it can be readily held in one hand and the product can all be easily removed using a fork or spoon. As these products are meant to be consumed at one 'sitting', the lack of a reclosable lid is not an issue, although there is one brand that uses a snap-on resealable lid held in place by a full-length sleeve, which also provides tamper evidence and all-round decoration. Other than this, pots are decorated either by direct printing (screen, or dry offset letterpress) or by self-adhesive labels.

8.4.5 Bags, sachets, pouches, brick packs

These packs have been grouped together because they are all made from reels of film or laminate, which is then used to make the required pack type. The pack forming process can be carried out either as an integral part of the product filling line (usually vertical form, fill and seal) or as a separate operation by the packaging manufacturer and delivered flat-packed to the packer/filler. As a general rule, the former is faster and thus likely to be less expensive, but the latter offers more flexibility of shape and may offer greater security of pack seal. The packs are used in frozen, chilled and ambient conditions.

Bags and sachets are used to describe both pillow packs, which may be used for sauces and ingredients (e.g. rice) that are included in a composite meal, possibly packed in a carton or tray, and the side-gusseted packs used for complete frozen meals, e.g. Chinese stir-fry dishes. They can be designed to withstand the cooking process, e.g. boil-in-the bag products such as rice, and fish-in-sauce dishes, which use high-density polyethylene (HDPE) film, and sauces heated in the microwave. Pillow packs do not display well and are thus not an ideal choice to be used alone, whereas gusseted bags can be designed to stand up and serve as a standalone pack.

One of the most interesting developments in this group of packs is the stand-up retort pouch currently used for soups and sauces in both the chilled and long shelf life ambient sectors. As mentioned earlier, the retort pouch was introduced in the 1970s as a replacement for the metal can, but was not wholly acceptable at that time. Today's version is an improvement in that, among other factors, it addresses the problem of display on shelf. The technology of making stand-up pouches goes back to the 1960s and has been used for detergents and, with aseptic packaging systems, for fruit drinks. This has now been developed into the fully retort-stable pack, offering the benefit of improved taste over traditional canning, due to the shorter processing time needed. Laminates are available with and without aluminium foil, the latter offering transparency while still providing a good barrier to moisture and gases when coated with SiO_x (5).

With regard to consumer convenience, stand-up pouches are opened by tearing or cutting, and the all-plastic versions can be placed in the microwave oven to heat the product. Pouches used for dry products such as dried fruit are reclosed using zipper features, although to date this has not been extended to retort pouches owing to concerns that the zipper feature might not withstand the retorting process. The pouches can be fully printed, offering good graphic design potential and they can either be delivered ready made to the packer/filler or delivered as reels and formed on line. Thus they offer advantages in terms of storage space required for empty packs. One disadvantage in storage and distribution of filled packs, however, is that they have little or no resistance to compression and thus do not stack without the use of corrugated board cases or full-height trays, which increases the total pack cost. Nevertheless, this pack has potential for greater use as a replacement for the traditional can, as it is much lighter in weight, takes up less storage space in disposal and, overall, uses less packaging.

Brick packs are used for long shelf life ambient storage of soups and are made from laminates of paper, aluminium foil and thermoplastics for heat sealing. Their handy shape offers good stability on shelf and economical use of space in storage and distribution. They usually require scissors for opening and, as they are not easily reclosed, they are best used for portion sizes that are likely to be consumed all at once. Pack instructions state that the contents should be decanted for heating.

8.4.6 Printed board cartons and sleeves

The aluminium foil, ovenable board and plastics trays discussed earlier in this section are usually further packed into either printed cartons or sleeves. This additional board packaging has three broad purposes. One, it provides protection against physical damage such as puncturing of the lid, or squashing of the tray; two, it regularises the shape of the pack to improve stability in stacking during storage and display; and three, it provides an excellent printing surface to enhance the selling appeal of the product and provide the consumer with important information. Cartons also provide a light barrier, which may be required for some products.

Printed cartons are usually of the skillet type, with the ends glued in place, fully enclosing the tray inside and offering tamper evidence. Perforations provide easy-open features, such as tear strips. The six-sided format provides ample space for graphics and printed copy. Sleeves are more economical in use of board, but provide less protection against physical damage and less printable area. They also need some means of preventing the tray from falling out and this is usually achieved by 'kick in flaps' – two die-cut slots that allow sections of the sleeve to be turned inwards towards the tray, forming a retaining flap at each end. Both cartons and trays can be fully printed and board grades can be selected to give excellent finished effects such as smoothness and high gloss levels, as well as good performance during chilled or frozen storage and display.

8.5 Packaging Machine Considerations

Whatever type of pack is chosen for a ready meal product, inevitably it will encounter packaging machinery with varying degrees of automation, as part of the production and packing process. Indeed, some of the pack types discussed in the previous section cannot be assembled without fully automatic machinery and even relatively small-scale production will be automated in some way. It is therefore essential to consider the packaging machine and its requirements and interaction with the packaging materials.

The importance of the preservation/protection and containment roles of packaging has already been emphasised, and the packaging machine plays just as significant a part in the successful achievement of these roles as the correct selection of the packaging materials and formats. Crucially, it is the closing and sealing of the pack that directly impact upon its performance in these roles, as well as meeting consumer convenience in terms of ease of opening, and therefore this section will concentrate on the factors that affect closing and sealing. Of course, this does mean that the packaging machine has no impact on pack appearance and this is especially significant in vertical form, fill and seal operations, which can be designed to produce a number of different pack shapes, from simple pillow packs to gusseted and top-folded bags, to stand-up pouches and brick packs. For these pack types it is the pack forming process that determines how the finished packed product can be displayed and thus how it is presented to the consumer, as well as how it can be stored in the home.

Closing a pack is carried out by different methods, dependent upon the pack type, and for ready meals the methods can be broken down into three distinct categories. The first is by means of folding, such as the aluminium foil tray, where the rim is rolled down to secure the board lid in place; the second is a mechanical seal, such as the snap-on or screw-threaded cap used on plastic tubs; and the third is by means of heat sealing. For the first two methods, the most important factors affecting seal integrity are the dimensional accuracy of each of the packaging components and the correct alignment of closure to container during the packaging operation. Application pressure must be controlled to avoid compressing and damaging the container, and application torque is an important factor to consider when applying screw-threaded caps. Allowance must be made for backing off (loosening after application) of the cap, which will happen with thermoplastic materials owing to creep or cold flow, and the torque used to tighten the cap in place must be such that, when this loosening has occurred, the seal will still be intact and the user will be able to open the pack readily.

It is the third category of pack closing, that of heat sealing, that is probably the most critical and subject to the greatest number of variables that can affect the seal integrity of the pack. It is also the most common method of closing and sealing the types of pack used for ready meal packaging, including those that are required to be gas-tight and suitable for modified-atmosphere packaging, and hence it is of prime importance in assuring product preservation and safety for the consumer.

Heat sealing consists essentially of applying heat to the interface between two thermoplastic materials to the point where the interfacing layers soften, and at the same time applying pressure to the softened materials to effect a bond between them by fusion. As the heated layer cools, it hardens and a bond is developed. Both direct and indirect heating methods are used and the heat may be applied to the area to be bonded through one or both substrates. The thermoplastic layer can be a film, or an extrusion coating, hot melt coating or lacquer applied to another substrate.

From this brief description we can deduce the key factors that will affect the integrity of the seal obtained. Firstly, the correct amount of heat must be applied to the seal area and this can be affected by the machine, the material and the product. The machine must be capable of maintaining a consistent and reliable temperature across the entire sealing area of the pack and throughout the production period, and the achievable temperature range must be compatible with the softening point of the sealing material used – and vice-versa. It is essential that materials and machinery are designed to be compatible with one another. The length of time that heat is applied (the dwell time) is also critical: too short and the sealing layer will not reach the required temperature, too long and the sealing layer may become too soft and flow away from the seal area, as well as the more obvious disadvantage of slowing down the production line speed.

The packaging material must not distort when heated and its thermal conductivity must allow heat to penetrate through to the sealing interface and, at the same time, where bar sealing is used, the outer layer of the material must withstand the heat applied without shrinking or burning, especially of any surface print or lacquer that could pick off and lead to a build-up of charred material on the sealing head. Ideally, the material should be printed so that there is no ink in the sealing area; alternatively, a heat-resistant lacquer or film may be used as the outside layer. The sealing layer must be of sufficient thickness to provide the required degree of seal and of even thickness throughout. Also, there should be no creases or folds in the material as these not only interfere with heat transfer, but also provide channels for the transmission of moisture and gases, and, in the worst cases, for leakage of the product itself.

With regard to the product and its effect on the heat-sealing process, if it is very cold it will remove heat from the sealing area and allowance will have to be made for this; otherwise, the sealing surface may not reach its softening temperature. Conversely, if the product is filled hot, the time needed for the sealing layer to cool and harden to give a sufficiently strong bond may be increased. The nature of the product, e.g. dusty or fatty, and especially the presence of product in the heat-seal area, are other contributing factors to seal integrity, as seal contamination will interfere both with the conductivity of heat and the fusion of the two layers at the sealing surface. The use of an ionomer such as Du Pont's Surlyn®, which has excellent hot tack strength (forming a bond very rapidly) and the ability to seal through contaminants should be considered if contamination of the seal area cannot easily be eliminated (6).

The pressure applied must be even and sufficient to hold the sealing surfaces together, but not so great as to push the softened material away from the seal area. There may be little pressure adjustment possible but the machine factors controlling pressure should be understood, as should the compressibility of the packaging material and the hot tack of the sealing layer. This should be sufficient to initiate a bond as rapidly as possible and the bond should be strong enough to remain intact when the pressure is released. The extent to which this is achieved is also dependent on the ambient temperature and how quickly heat can be removed from the newly forming seal.

There are other factors that affect seal integrity, which are described below, although this section does not claim to present an exhaustive list. One factor is the dimensional accuracy of the packaging material in terms of reel width, core, evenness of winding and print registration, all of which will affect the smooth travel of the material through the machine, as will the coefficient of friction. There should be minimum wander and correct cut-off length, ensuring that lid and base webs are correctly aligned. The size and position of the seal area must be designed to provide the correct degree of closure for the pack type, and this is especially critical for modified-atmosphere packs, which usually have a fairly large seal area. Environmental conditions of temperature, humidity and air cleanliness will also affect seal quality. Finally, the packaging machine, its cleanliness and state of adjustment and maintenance, and the level of expertise and understanding of the line operators are very important factors.

Consideration must be given to pack inspection as part of the packaging line operation. In addition to weight checks, metal detection and inspection for foreign body contamination, seal integrity must be checked, and this is usually done by applying pressure or vacuum to detect any incomplete seals. Checking can be done on line using automatic systems that carry out a non-destructive test on every pack, or by statistical sampling of packs from the line. Whichever method is used, there must be a clear procedure for both the testing and action required in the event of failure.

8.6 Secondary Packaging Requirements

The discussion so far has concentrated mainly on primary packaging, i.e. the packaging that surrounds the product when it is sold, and which is 'conceived so as to constitute a sales unit to the final user or consumer at the point of purchase' (7). This includes both the packaging in direct contact with the product and components such as sleeves and cartons, which have already been discussed. Secondary packaging is that used to group primary packs together in convenient units for ease of handling and, where required, ease of display. While the primary pack must be robust enough to withstand handling on the filling line and individual handling by the consumer while on display, during the journey home and in home storage and use, it is the secondary pack that is usually relied upon to provide protection against the physical hazards of the storage and distribution environment.

The role of packaging in providing protection has already been mentioned, including typical hazards in the storage and distribution environment. The selection of the optimum secondary pack format can be made only when the likely hazards have been evaluated, and it must be understood that not all hazards can be accommodated within a practical and cost-effective solution.

Once the likely hazards are understood, the choice of secondary packaging materials and format depends largely on the fragility of the primary pack and to what extent it can withstand these hazards on its own. It is probably true to say that the original ready meal pack, the metal can, is far more robust than its modern-day competitors and thus makes fewer demands on its secondary packaging. For the range of primary packs already discussed in this chapter, typical secondary packaging formats are corrugated board cases and corrugated board trays covered with shrink wrap film. There is also some use of unsupported shrink wrap film. Some retailers also use their own style of transit packaging – returnable plastic trays, which are designed to provide compression resistance when stacked loaded with product and which can be fully nested for stacking when empty and returned to the packer/filler. Whichever method is used, there must be sufficient protection against squashing and excessive pack-to-pack movement, which could cause scuffing and affect seal quality.

Good secondary packaging design is essential not just for product protection but also for sound economic reasons, as one of the significant costs in the food sector is the cost of moving goods. Primary and secondary packs should be designed so that a maximum number of products can be safely transported as a single unit, i.e. on a pallet, tray or roll cage. Secondary pack labelling is also vital, as the pack must be readily identifiable during order picking, which is usually a very busy and fast-moving environment. To avoid costly mistakes and to assist in good stock control, all information must be clearly legible, whether designed to be read by the human eye or electronically.

The choice of secondary packaging format greatly influences the ease and safety of moving goods and, most importantly, of displaying goods in store. Shelf-ready trays or cases that can be easily converted to trays offer the opportunity for designing and therefore influencing the display format. Not only can shelves be restocked quickly, thus maintaining consistent shelf presence, but the product can be displayed consistently in the same manner, optimising its appearance for maximum impact, to attract the consumer and effect the sale.

8.7 Developing the Packaging

This section has been included to provide the reader with a checklist of factors to be considered during the process of developing a suitable pack for a ready meal product. It is by no means an inarguable blueprint for the development process, but hopefully it will encourage a logical approach, which will go some way towards implementing a successful new product introduction. It assumes that the market demand for the product has been established and the target consumer identified, i.e. there is some reasonably firm information regarding the quantity of product likely to be required.

First of all, a thorough review of the product demands is required. To design a cost-effective pack that performs well throughout all stages of its life, it is essential to understand what are the critical properties of the product. What are the factors that will result in its becoming unacceptable to the consumer? For example, is it highly sensitive to exposure to oxygen or light; will it deteriorate by drying out, or by absorbing moisture; is a liquid barrier critical; is it easily broken (for example a pastry case)? Alongside these fundamental questions it is also useful to consider what features would enhance the appeal of the product to the target consumer. For example, if it is attractive to look at and not light-sensitive, it may be appropriate to consider transparent packaging so that the consumer can instantly recognise it. The way in which the product can be carried home and stored in the fridge, freezer or cupboard should be considered, as well as how the pack can be opened/closed and whether or not the pack can be designed to act as the cooking vessel.

When the packed product leaves the production line it will enter the distribution chain, where it will be exposed to a number of potentially hazardous events, such as transport, stacking in warehouses and manual handling during order-picking, display in store and being taken home by the consumer. A good understanding of the likely hazards during these events is necessary, including measurement of temperature and humidity. The greater the understanding of the nature and likelihood of the hazards, the more closely the pack can be designed to meet actual and not imagined performance requirements. This is turn should provide the most cost-effective and environmentally efficient solution.

Once the demands of the product and the hazards to which it will be exposed are identified, potential packaging materials and formats can be considered, although the choice may be constrained. For example, it may be that there is already an established format for that product type, in which case the decision may be made to follow this trend. Alternatively, there could be a deliberate stance to deviate from the norm, as a point of difference. The packaging machinery available may also inform the choice of pack, or a decision may be taken to use a contract packer with alternative facilities. The time available to launch will be another deciding factor, especially in this highly competitive sector, where 'speed to market' is vital. Some pack formats may be ruled out on cost grounds.

Potential solutions for all levels of packaging should be considered when making decisions. The total cost of the product in this sector is significantly influenced by the cost of moving goods, so it is important to design in good pallet utilisation from the outset. What is being sought is cost-effective performance across the total pack and it could be that a minor improvement to a primary packaging component may dramatically reduce the amount of secondary packaging needed.

A reliable source of supply of packaging materials is essential, with suppliers able to contribute to the development process. Approved suppliers should operate to an acceptable quality and hygiene standard, such as the British Retail Consortium/Institute of Packaging Technical Standard and Protocol for Companies Manufacturing and Supplying Food Packaging Materials for Retailer Branded Products (8).

A programme of testing will be required to decide between potential solutions and to confirm acceptability. This may include market testing, especially if the pack is being promoted as offering special features, e.g. easy-open, to confirm that it does perform as expected under the likely conditions of use. Testing by simulating the conditions in the distribution environment, using a pack of known performance as a benchmark, should also be conducted, and the extent of the test programme will depend on how new the concept being developed is. Specifications and standards must be in place before production commences and this can only be done when the required level of performance has been determined.

Once pack formats are finalised, development of graphic design and artwork can be completed, taking into account the relevant legislation with respect to labelling and consumer protection. The pack must provide information, which must be easily understood and legible, and nothing about the pack must be misleading. Colour plays an important role in product recognition, and colour consistency in printed packaging materials should be controlled.

During the development process, product cost, including development costs such as market studies, special tooling and print origination, must be monitored, along with the timetable to ensure a timely launch. Also, there is a legal requirement for companies placing goods on the market to comply with EC Directive 94/62 on Packaging and Packaging Waste, implemented in the United Kingdom via the Producer Responsibility Obligations (Packaging Waste) Regulations and the Packaging (Essential Requirements) Regulations. The latter calls for packaging to be 'the minimum adequate amount to maintain the necessary level of safety, hygiene and acceptance for the packed product and for the consumer' and this means understanding why you are using your chosen pack format and materials and being able to justify your decisions.

8.8 Future Trends

The popularity of ready meals as a product sector will undoubtedly continue to grow, and with that growth will come greater demands for consumer convenience features. Packaging that offers a simple way of opening a hot pack, such as a means by which the heat-sealed film lid on a tray breaks when the product inside has reached the required temperature, will present a significant benefit. Packaging that gives a clearly visible sign that the product is cooked, such as a colour change, will provide the consumer with reassurance that the meal is ready. For the entertaining, or dinner party market, there is a place for the pack that opens without leaving a residue on the container rim and which provides a visually appealing serving dish.

There will probably be even more use of modified-atmosphere packaging, to limit the use of chemical preservatives and appeal to the health-conscious consumer. This will place more emphasis on gas-tight sealing systems, how they are achieved, checked on the packaging line and maintained throughout the storage life of the product. There is possibly a role here for a visual measure or indicator of freshness in the pack, to reassure the consumer that the product is of the required quality.

The environmental acceptability of packaging both to the consumer and with regard to legislation, will continue to put pressure on packaging reduction. Light weighting of all materials will continue, although this must be balanced against the need not to compromise other performance criteria, such as product protection and the need for packaging to run efficiently on automatic packaging machinery. Removal of packaging components, such as sleeves and cartons from plastic trays, discussed earlier, will probably become more prominent, as manufacturers seek to limit total packaging material usage.

In conclusion, the demands of the ready meals market will continue to present challenges to packaging technology. Technologists in the plastics, aluminium foil and paper and board sectors, along with functional and graphic packaging designers and machinery specialists, will continue to rise to these challenges, and the producers and sellers of ready meals must be ever open-minded to packaging innovation.

References

1. Ekco Packaging Limited. Latest News at www. ekcopackaging.com.
2. Ekco Packaging Limited. Technical Data Sheet *Heat Seal Film to Plain Aluminium Smoothwall Foils.*
3. Aluminium Foil Container Manufacturers Association. *Foil trays in the microwave.*
4. Sheahan M. *Active and passive packaging collaborate to boost shelf life.* Packaging News, December 2001, 1-2.
5. Hunt L. *Standing room only.* Packaging Today, July 2001, 30-2.
6. Surlyn® packaging resins, www.dupont.com/packaging/products/resins.
7. EC Directive 94/62, Packaging and Packaging Waste.
8. The Stationery Office, www.clicktso.com.

Bibliography and Further Reading

Emblem A., Emblem H. (Editors). *Fundamentals of Packaging Technology.* Melton Mowbray, The Institute of Packaging. 1997.

Emblem A., Emblem H. *Packaging Prototypes II.* Switzerland, RotoVision SA. 2000.

Gould G. *New Methods of Food Preservation.* Chapman & Hall, London. 1995.

Kilcast D., Subramaniam P. (Editors). *The Stability and Shelf-life of Food.* Cambridge, Woodhead Publishing Limited. 2000.

Rooney M. (Editor). *Active Food Packaging.* Chapman & Hall, London. 1995.

The following Web sites also provide useful reference material for this subject:

www.alcanpackaging.com
www.dotpackaging.com/news/innovation
www.ekcopackaging.com
www.packagingdigest.com
www.pactiv.com

Note

Whilst every effort has been made in writing this Chapter to ensure that the material is accurate, no legal liability is accepted for any errors or omissions, or any conclusions drawn from the information. Information is given on the understanding that it must be verified by means of trials, before being implemented. No responsibility is accepted for such trials.

9. THE UK READY MEALS MARKET

Danuta Tomoszek

9.1 Introduction

The ready meals market consists of three main segments: chilled, frozen and ambient, of which the largest is chilled (Table 9.I).

TABLE 9.I
UK ready meals market, 1999

	Estimated market value (£m)
Chilled	710
Frozen	550
Ambient	42

Until 1997, the frozen segment took the largest share of the market in the UK, but chilled has been growing at a much faster rate, and now accounts for 55% of the total market. Frozen accounts for 42%, and ambient only around 3%.

Figure 9.1 shows the value of the total UK ready meals market, from 1995 to 1999. The chilled ready meals segment is clearly growing the fastest – by around 13% in 1999, and by around 20% in 1998. There are two key trends driving this growth rate:

i) Consumer demand – increasing demand from consumers for convenient meal solutions, driven by factors such as the increase in the percentage of women who work (now up to 55%), a decline in cooking skills, a growing number of single-person households and greater disposable income.

   Single-person households are growing steadily, and now account for around 28% of all households. They are forecast to become the major demographic group within the next few years, overtaking two-person households, which currently account for around 33% of total UK households.

Disposable income has increased steadily over the last few years; it rose between 2% and 3% a year during most of the 1990s.

ii) Retailer push – the major multiples now offer consumers significantly wider product ranges and better quality products.

The largest four retailers in the market now have product ranges of around 300 products, including meal centres, side dishes such as vegetables, rice or noodles, and associated snacks or starters such as onion bhajias, samosas, spring rolls, ribs and onion rings.

The quality of the products available has also improved significantly. A few years ago, Marks & Spencer, where chilled ready meals were first widely available, was regarded as the only place to go to buy a good quality ready meal. More recently, the major multiples have been catching up and are also considered by consumers to offer good quality products.

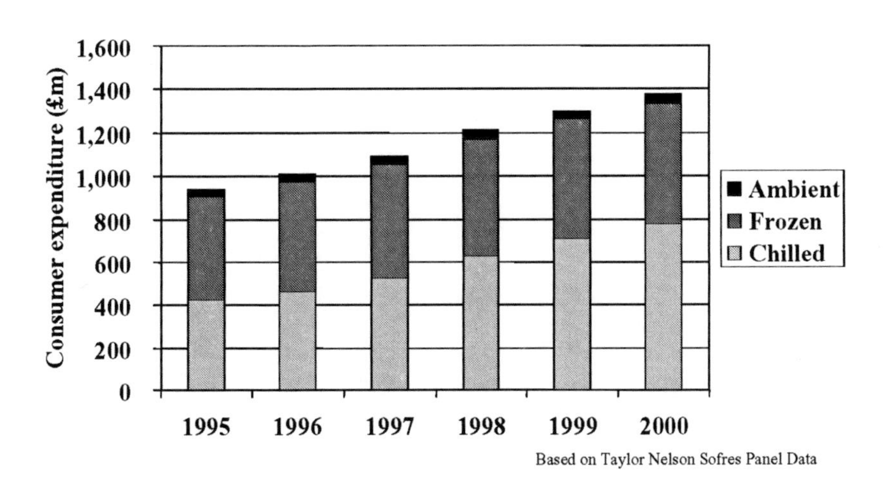

Fig. 9.1. UK ready meals market, 1995–2000

The frozen market has not seen any significant growth over the last few years, compared with the big increases seen in the chilled market.

Consumers generally perceive frozen meals to be of a lower quality than chilled meals, and so are usually prepared to pay less. Birds Eye Wall's has been running a big advertising campaign to highlight the quality of its frozen products, and it will be interesting to see if this type of activity, combined with the expected growth in home delivery, which is probably more suited to frozen than fresh products, start to create growth in the frozen market again.

9.2 UK Market Shares by Type of Ready Meal

This section covers the chilled and frozen ready meals markets. The ambient market is not included as it is a very small part of the overall market, and segment share information is not reliable.

9.2.1 Chilled ready meals

The chilled ready meals market is generally segmented according to the ethnic origin of the meal. Figure 9.2 shows the chilled ready meals market for 1999 segmented into the various ethnic styles of meal.

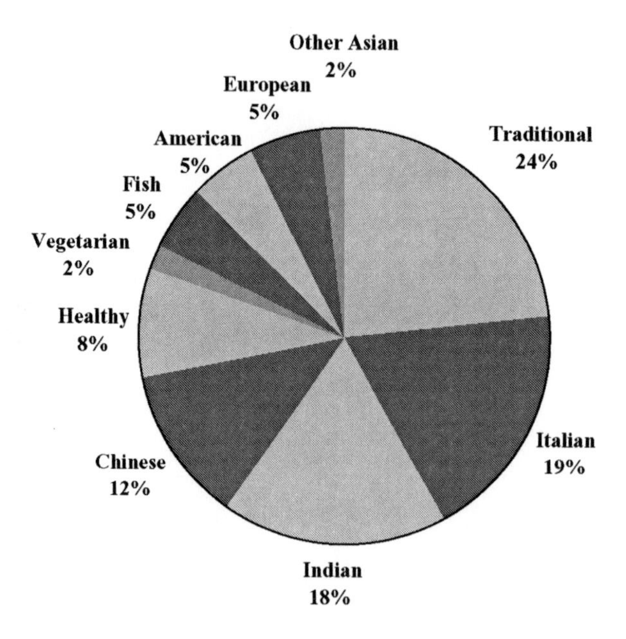

Fig. 9.2. UK chilled ready meals market by cuisine, 1999 (£ consumer expenditure)

Still the most popular types of meal are traditional-style meat or vegetable dishes, such as stews, potato-topped pies, cauliflower cheese and mashed potato. Together, these types of product account for 23% of the total market. Next largest are Italian dishes, i.e. pasta-based meals. Third are Indian meals, including accompaniments such as rice and vegetable side dishes. The fourth major segment is Chinese.

The smaller segments are healthy, vegetarian, fish, American, European and other Asian. However, the healthy segment is growing fast, and is likely to become as big as Chinese in the next couple of years. This growth is due to the much greater availability of reduced-fat meals, combined with consumers' increasing concern about the fat content of the products that they are eating.

9.2.2 *Frozen ready meals*

The frozen ready meals market is generally segmented according to whether the main ingredient of the meal is meat, fish or other/vegetable. Figure 9.3 shows the UK chilled ready meals market for 1999 segmented into the main ingredient of the meal.

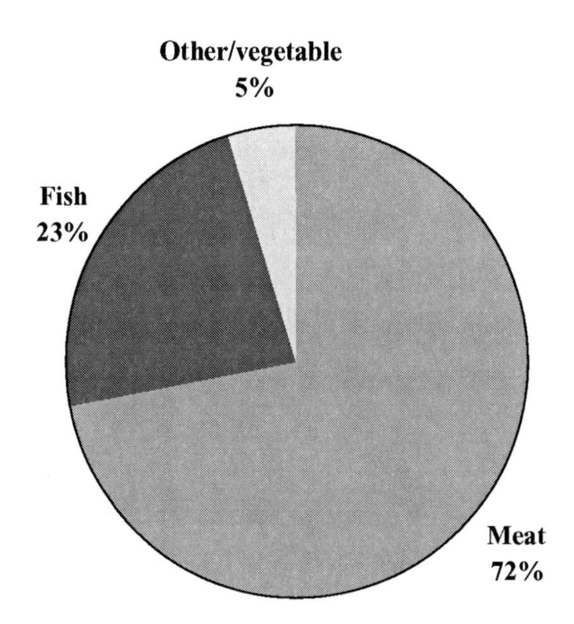

Based on Taylor Nelson Sofres Panel Data

Fig. 9.3. UK frozen ready meals market by cuisine, 1999 (£ consumer expenditure)

By far the biggest segment of the market is that for meat-based meals, which accounted for 72% of total consumer expenditure in this market in 1999. Fish is a much bigger segment in the frozen ready meals market than in the chilled market, because of potato-topped fish pies, which have been a consumer favourite for years. However, this segment is now declining as consumers are being offered a greater choice of meat-based meals, including all the international cuisine options such as Indian, Chinese and American, as well as traditional British meals.

9.3 UK Retailer Market Shares

This section covers the chilled and frozen ready meals markets. The ambient market is not included as it is a very small part of the overall market, and share information is not reliable.

Market shares for the major retailers vary considerably between the chilled and frozen ready meals markets. For example, Marks & Spencer is much stronger in the chilled market than in the frozen, as it concentrates heavily on fresh foods, to draw people into its shops. Iceland is strong only in the frozen market, as it specialises in frozen food. Discount and convenience outlets have a much higher share of the frozen market than the chilled market, as they typically stock a much wider range of frozen meals than fresh. This is probably due to historical reasons, as the frozen market was bigger than the chilled market, and because it is easier to stock frozen products as they have a longer shelf life.

For comparison, the overall retailer market shares are shown in Table 9.II.

Table 9.II
Retailer market share for chilled and frozen ready meals
Share of total consumer expenditure (52 weeks to November 1999)

	%
Tesco	16
Sainsbury	13
Asda	11
Safeway	7
Somerfield/Kwiksave	6
Morrison	3
Marks & Spencer	2
Iceland	2

Source: Taylor Nelson Sofres Panel Data

9.3.1 Chilled ready meals

The multiple retailers have the largest shares of the chilled ready meals market. Figure 9.4 shows chilled ready meals market shares for 1999.

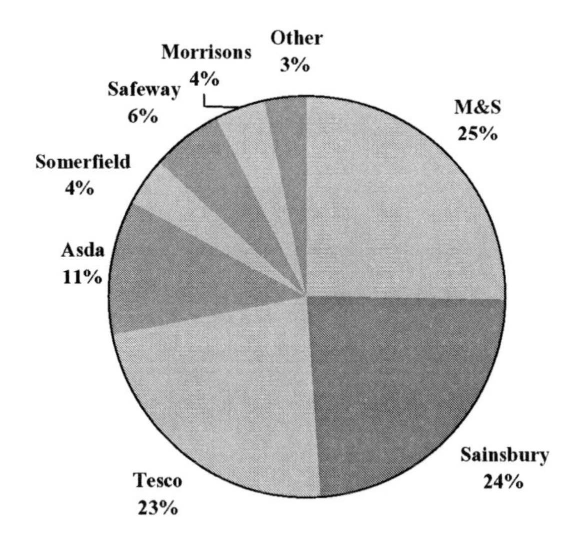

Based on Taylor Nelson Sofres Panel Data

Figure 9.4. UK chilled ready meals market shares, 1999 (£ consumer expenditure)

Marks & Spencer, the original pioneer of the chilled ready meal, still has the largest market share, with around 25%. Sainsbury's has the second largest share with 24% and Tesco is third largest with 23%. Still some way behind, but growing fast, is Asda with 11%. The rest of the major multiples, Safeway, Somerfield and Morrison, all have between 4 and 6%. Very little of the market is through conveniences stores.

Both Marks & Spencer and Sainsbury's are strong in the chilled ready meals market, with shares that exceed their overall market shares (Tesco is now the number one retailer in terms of overall market share in value terms).

9.3.2 Frozen ready meals

The multiple retailers are again strong in the frozen ready meals market, but Iceland is also very strong. Figure 9.5 shows frozen ready meals market shares in the UK for 1999.

Tesco has the largest market share, in line with its overall retailer share, and Iceland is the number two, with a 16% share, due to its strong position in the frozen foods market. Sainsbury's has 15% and Asda has 14%. At 8% each are Safeway and Somerfield. Marks & Spencer has a small share, at 2%, as it concentrates on chilled foods. 'Others' are significant at 18%; this category includes discount and convenience stores.

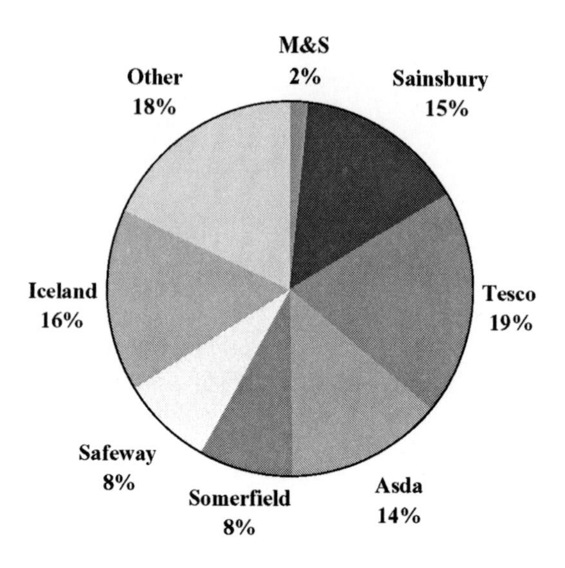

Fig. 9.5. UK frozen ready meals market shares, 1999 (£ consumer expenditure)

9.4 Key UK Ready Meal Manufacturers

There is a significant number of key manufacturers supplying the UK ready meals market, although, with the major multiples currently going through a rationalisation of their supplier base, in order to reduce costs, the number of suppliers is likely to fall.

9.4.1 Chilled ready meals

The chilled market is virtually all own-label, with suppliers to Marks & Spencer, Sainsbury, Tesco and Asda accounting for over 80% of the total market. The biggest suppliers include the following:

- Oscar Mayer
- Geest
- Northern Foods
- Ferndale Foods

- Food Enterprises
- Katsouris
- Noon
- Pennine Foods
- RF Brookes
- Cavaghan & Gray
- Rowan Foods
- S & A Foods

9.4.2 *Frozen ready meals*

The frozen ready meals market is split between own-label and branded products, which are much bigger in the frozen than in the chilled market.

The biggest manufacturer in the frozen ready meals market is Birds Eye Wall's, with Findus in second place, Ross third and Heinz fourth.

9.5 UK Retailers' Product Ranges

9.5.1 *Chilled ready meals*

There were around 1,500 chilled ready meal products available on the market as at December 1999, the vast majority of which were own-label products from the major supermarkets, including Marks & Spencer. The number of products on the market has increased significantly over the last couple of years, as all the retailers have reviewed and extended their ranges; for example, the number of products on the market rose by around 40% during 1999.

Marks & Spencer has by far the largest range, with around 350 products. Tesco and Sainsbury have steadily increased the size of their ranges over the last 2 years, and now have around 250 products each. Asda is the next largest, with around 200 products, and Waitrose, Safeway, Somerfield and Morrison have between 100 and 150 products each. Obviously, not every branch of each supermarket will stock the complete range, owing to shelf space constraints.

There are very few branded products available in the chilled ready meals market, and those that are available are not widely known brands. Examples include the following ranges:-

- Noon Indian meals
- Sutherland Value and 95% Fat Free ranges
- A La Carte 95% Fat Free range
- Bighams range of raw international-style meals

More common are retailers' sub-brands, of which there are a significant number, as retailers seek to respond to consumers' desire for products that reflect their personality.

Marks & Spencer has several sub-brands, including:-

- Homestyle – traditional British meals and side dishes such as casseroles and cauliflower cheeses.
- Café Specials – a range of bistro-type dishes, including side dishes, breads, cold meats, salads, desserts and even wine, which are all merchandised together, to offer consumers a very easy way of selecting a complete meal.
- Connoisseur – an upmarket range covering various products, again merchandised in a block.

Sainsbury also offers several sub-brands, including:-

- Fresh Creations – a range of ready to cook "meal kits", with a meat meal centre and side dishes packaged together.
- Be Good to Yourself - a range of fat-reduced meals.

Tesco offers sub-brands covering the two extremes of quality/price:-

- Mega Value – a range of low-price, large-portion meals.
- Finest – Tesco's range of high-quality products aims to offer consumers restaurant-quality meals.

9.5.2 Frozen ready meals

There is a much smaller range of frozen meals available compared with the number of chilled ready meals products on the market, which is where the retailers are currently concentrating their efforts. The chilled market is led by the retailers, and the frozen market is led by the brands.

In terms of value market share, the frozen market is predominantly branded, with Birds Eye Wall's Menu Master brand taking the biggest share. The main frozen brands include the following:-

- Birds Eye Menu Master
- Findus Crosse & Blackwell
- Heinz Weightwatchers, a range of reduced-fat, calorie-counted meals.

- Ross Young's
- Dolmio, a range of pasta meals, launched on the strength of the brand in the ambient pasta sauces market.
- Bluecrest
- Rhodes to Home, a range of meals endorsed by the chef Gary Rhodes.

9.6 Summary

The chilled ready meals market has overtaken the frozen market in terms of value, and continues to grow at a much faster rate. The major retailers see the chilled market as more important than frozen in tempting consumers into their stores, and are also starting to integrate chilled ready meals into "lifestyle" ranges of products to create complete meals for target groups of consumers.

The chilled market is growing by around 10-15% a year, whereas the frozen market is more or less static in real value terms.

The chilled market is led by the retailers, and the frozen market is led by a number of brands. Retailers' market shares do not necessarily line up with their overall market shares. Marks & Spencer has the largest share of the chilled market, and Tesco has the largest share of the frozen market.

The home meal replacement market is just starting to develop, and the major retailers are ideally placed to take advantage of the growth in demand for good quality, pre-prepared meals to take home.

10. THE MICROBIOLOGICAL SAFETY AND QUALITY OF READY MEALS

Alec Kyriakides and Steve Batchford

10.1 Introduction

The microbiological safety and quality of ready meals are dependent on a variety of factors, most notably raw material quality, processing conditions, hygienic manufacture and shelf life. Ready meals encompass a wide variety of products made from a wide range of raw ingredients that generate a complex microflora in a highly variable product matrix. Safety and stability come from a broad understanding of the spoilage and pathogenic microorganisms likely to pose a hazard to the product, mechanisms by which such organisms can be kept out of the food or, if present, how the production process or product formulation affects microbial growth and survival. This chapter focuses on the microbiological issues that may affect ready meal manufacture, encompassing raw material hazards and controls, processing control and final product considerations. It also considers the importance of hygienic control and shelf life in contributing to the microbiological safety and quality of ready meals. Finally, details are given of a variety of microorganisms of significance to ready meals together with factors affecting their growth and survival.

10.2 Raw Materials

The raw materials used in the manufacture of ready meals have a large influence on the microbiological safety and quality of the finished product. The diverse nature of ready meals necessitates using a huge array of raw materials sourced from countries throughout the world. Materials will encompass all food industry groups and, with such a wide range of ingredients, quality assurance programmes aimed at identifying hazards and implementing appropriate controls are essential to assure product safety and quality.

10.2.1 Assessing the risk and identifying the controls

The application of hazard analysis techniques is particularly helpful in identifying those materials that may represent a greater microbiological risk and in deciding where control is best implemented (see Chapter 5).

Each raw material should be assessed to determine the microbiological hazards that may occur, whether they could present a risk in the final product and, if so, whether appropriate controls exist at the raw material supplier or during the subsequent manufacturing process of the ready meal to reduce the hazard to an acceptable level.

Answers to simple questions such as where are the raw materials sourced from, how are they made, how are they stored and what is their shelf life can give significant insight into the microbiological hazards likely to be associated with them. In addition, subsequent processing conditions need to be taken into account. Raw materials that are to be subjected to a full microbiological destruction process such as a cook, e.g. 70 °C for 2 minutes, would hold less of a concern in relation to the presence of vegetative pathogens such as *Salmonella* or *Listeria* than those that are destined to have little or no further cooking prior to sale and consumption. However, whilst the presence of such organisms may not be of major concern if the product is to be fully cooked, it is critical to remember that such processing is usually designed to achieve a specified reduction in microbial contamination, e.g. 6 log reduction. Excessive levels of contamination may compromise the safety of the finished product as the starting level of contamination may exceed the capacity of the process to reduce them to a safe number.

For raw materials intended to be cooked during processing, the biggest concern relates to the potential presence of microbial toxins produced by organisms such as *Staphylococcus aureus*, which may have developed in the raw material as a result of excessive growth under poorly controlled storage conditions or in their processing. Most microbial toxins will survive the relatively mild processing employed in the manufacture of many ready meals and, if they are present in the raw materials, they will inevitably remain in the final product.

Many ready meals are manufactured using processes that will have little or no effect in reducing the level of contaminating microorganisms present in the raw materials, such as cold mixed products, or those where the ingredient is added to a previously cooked product. In such circumstances, the presence of even low levels of contaminating pathogens such as *Salmonella* may present a significant hazard to the consumer of the finished product. Therefore, the focus for safety must be the procedures in place at the raw material supplier that ensure control of such hazards.

These considerations need to be equally applied to spoilage microorganisms, high levels of which in the raw material may affect the quality of the finished product in a number of ways. For example, excessive levels of the organism may survive the process and go on subsequently to grow and spoil the final product. Alternatively, high levels may already have caused raw material deterioration, resulting in off-flavours or product breakdown that becomes noticeable only during subsequent processing or in the final product.

The nature of the microbiological controls of raw materials can be established only after due consideration is given to the factors detailed above which, should be designed to identify which organisms are likely to be of concern to the final product.

10.2.2 Raw material assurance programmes

If a raw material is identified as representing a microbiological risk in relation to the subsequent safety or quality of the product, then control of the raw material is absolutely essential. Guidance relating to the control of specific microbiological hazards in a variety of food products is given in other texts (1-3). Some key points that should be included in raw material assurance programmes are detailed in Fig. 10.1.

Traceability of the raw material

Operation by the raw material supplier of a hazard analysis approach to food safety management

Knowledge of the processing and critical controlling factors for the material

Agreed specification with the raw material supplier

Raw material verification checks

Audit of the raw material supplier to review process control

Fig. 10.1. Key points for raw material assurance programmes

The level of risk that the material represents to the final product must be used to determine the stringency with which each of the above should be applied. It is not possible to cover all potential hazards with the wide variety of raw materials used in ready meal manufacture, but the broad hazards associated with key raw material product groups are detailed below.

10.2.3 Chilled raw materials

The majority of products that are stored chilled are, by their very nature, perishable. Such products usually have microorganisms present that would grow rapidly if stored under ambient conditions and either spoil the product or make it unsafe to eat owing to the production of toxins. Refrigerated storage is designed to reduce the rate at which such organisms grow, thereby prolonging the shelf life. Care must be taken with such products to ensure that they are stored for the appropriate time and under effective temperature control. Temperature abuse can lead to product deterioration and growth of pathogenic bacteria.

The principal hazard presented by properly produced perishable raw materials come from extensive shelf lives or from temperature abuse during storage. Of greatest concern are those microorganisms capable of growth at low temperatures (psychrotrophic growth), which include the potential pathogens *Clostridium botulinum*, *Bacillus cereus* and *Listeria monocytogenes*, together with a variety of spoilage microorganisms. If the raw ingredient is to be further cooked, vegetative organisms such as *Listeria* may be of less concern. However, spore-forming organisms such as *C. botulinum* and *B. cereus*, which can grow and produce toxin, need to be fully considered, although reported foodborne illness caused by both organisms is predominantly associated with temperature abuse rather than psychrotrophic growth. The toxin produced by *C. botulinum* is not exceptionally heat-stable but it will survive the mild processing applied to many ready meals. However, even if cooking temperatures were sufficient to destroy it, it is unacceptable to rely on cooking to destroy such an extreme hazard as botulinum toxin. Clearly, the raw material storage conditions or shelf life must be controlled to prevent hazards such as *L. monocytogenes*, *C. botulinum* and *B. cereus* from growing to unacceptable levels.

Listeria would be considered a potential hazard in a variety of refrigerated raw materials, such as cooked meats, soft cheese, shellfish, prepared salad vegetables and other neutral-pH chilled products, which may be prone to post-processing contamination at the raw material producer. *C. botulinum* would equally be of concern in cooked meats, shellfish and chilled extended life processed vegetables such as unacidified garlic purée, whilst *B. cereus* may be of concern in neutral-pH dairy products and highly spiced materials.

In general, the shorter the shelf life of the raw material and the lower the temperature of storage the better will be the microbiological quality and safety. Any perishable raw ingredient allocated a shelf life of greater than 10 days under refrigeration temperatures (<5 °C) should be considered to be of potential concern in relation to the possible presence of high levels of *L. monocytogenes* or psychrotrophic strains of *C. botulinum* or *B. cereus*. Such materials should have clearly established controlling factors, e.g. pH, water activity, etc., capable of preventing the growth of such organisms to high levels, or the shelf life should be restricted.

Some raw materials, such as fresh fish and meat, are highly perishable and, although most often associated with spoilage, particular care must be taken with some of these products to ensure safety. For example, scombroid fish such as tuna and mackerel contain high amounts of the amino acid histidine in their flesh, which can be converted to the toxic amine histamine by bacterial growth, if stored for too long at 5–8 °C or if temperature-abused for short periods. The toxin is heat-stable and gives rise to scombrotoxin or histamine poisoning when the final product is consumed. Likewise, the increased propensity to store raw meats and fish under vacuum packing to extend raw material shelf life can provide conditions for the growth of psychrotrophic strains of *C. botulinum*, and such hazards must be accounted for in any hazard analysis.

In addition to the microbial hazards, it should be remembered that subsequent processing of refrigerated raw ingredients such as cooking must take account of the temperature of the raw material. The raw material temperature must be checked prior to applying a cooking process to ensure that it is not lower than the minimum necessary to achieve a full cook. (See section 10.3.4.)

10.2.4 Dried raw materials

A large number of ingredients are sourced in their dry state as this allows longer shelf life and easier storage. The most common dry ingredients include herbs and spices, often sourced from areas where control of environmental contaminants is rudimentary. The benefits of dried materials from a microbial perspective is that, providing the water activity of the dried ingredient is sufficiently low, most microbial pathogens cannot grow. Water activity is a measure of the water available to microorganisms and not merely the water content of the food. *S. aureus* is the bacterial pathogen capable of growth at the lowest water activity (*ca* 0.86), although moulds can grow at levels down to *ca* 0.60.

It should be remembered that low water activity does not destroy pathogenic microorganisms unless some physical process is used to achieve the drying, i.e. high temperature (>65 °C). Indeed, *Salmonella* can survive for months and even years in dried products, and has caused many outbreaks due to the consumption of dried foods, including milk powder, chocolate and herbs and spices.

The key issues for the control of dried foods are consideration of the nature of the raw material and the processing conditions used to dry the product. The raw materials may themselves be subject to contamination during growing and harvesting, or the method of drying may result in contamination or even proliferation of contaminants. For example, sun drying products in poorly controlled conditions may allow significant contamination from environmental sources such as animals and insects, both of which may be sources or vectors of microbial pathogens. Drying high-moisture, neutral-pH products at warm temperatures under uncontrolled conditions may allow proliferation of organisms such as *S. aureus*, leading to the production of heat-stable toxin. Such hazards need to be considered during the hazard analysis exercise of each production process for raw materials used in the manufacture of ready meals.

Dried ingredients should be stored in dry, pest-free storage areas. Care must be taken when handling potentially contaminated dried materials such as spices, as dust can carry contaminants from the raw material handling areas to finished product areas, if conditions of segregation are not appropriate.

Dried ingredients usually harbour high levels of general microorganisms, including sporeforming microorganisms such as *Bacillus* species and moulds, as these organisms are more tolerant to dry, dusty conditions. The microbial loading of dried ingredients may need to be monitored if such loading is likely to affect the final product safety or stability.

It should be remembered that any heat process applied to a material that has low water activity will be significantly less effective at destroying microbial contaminants than if the material is brought to a high water activity. The absence of water significantly protects microorganisms from thermal destruction and, to achieve the same level of destruction at low water activity, e.g. a_w 0.90, the heat process required will need to be approximately ten times longer than at high water activities, e.g. 0.99; this will vary significantly dependent on the material and the hazard. If a process is reliant on heat processing dry materials for safety, then it is recommended that challenge tests are conducted in research facilities with the appropriate hazard to establish the minimum process necessary for the reliable destruction of the hazard.

As the products are dried, the potential exists to apply positive release testing (both chemical and microbiological) to the batch before acceptance or use, although such checks have a low statistical chance of detecting small amounts of contamination in a batch and must be viewed as only small components of the raw material assurance programme.

10.2.5 Frozen materials

Like drying, freezing effectively prevents the growth of contaminating microorganisms and psychrotrophic microbial pathogens are only capable of growth at temperatures just below 0 °C. All microbial growth ceases below about –10 °C but, like drying, freezing cannot be relied upon to destroy contaminating microorganisms.

The nature of the raw material being frozen, and the freezing process, are important considerations in relation to raw material safety and quality. Enzymes, including those derived from microorganisms, can remain active and cause product deterioration if freezing is not carried out and maintained effectively.

Care must be taken when cooking frozen raw materials to ensure that they are fully defrosted before applying the heat process, and clear conditions must be established to ensure that this is carried out effectively. Monitoring of raw material temperature prior to cooking is essential and this must not be below the established minimum demonstrated to allow an effective cook. (See (process validation later in this chapter) section 10.3.4.).

Like dried products, positive release testing (both chemical and microbiological) could be applied to batches of frozen product before acceptance or use, although such tests must not be viewed as more than a minor verification check.

10.2.6 Traditional products

The hazards associated with many products received as raw materials for ready meal manufacture are more difficult to assess because they are traditional in nature, and the inherent hazards and controls are not clearly established. Many fermented products fall into this category, such as cheeses, salamis, dried meats, oriental sauces, etc.

Key principles to apply to the safety of these products are to look for procedures that exist to ensure control of the fermentation stage and to ensure stability of the final product in relation to growth of pathogens.

The key hazard in the fermentation stage with these products is usually *S. aureus,* which can grow and produce a heat-stable toxin if the fermentation stage is not controlled. In such situations, procedures should exist for monitoring the activity of the fermentation using pH and acidity, and remedial measures should be specified if the fermentation does not follow an established profile.

Higher-risk fermented products such as raw milk cheese and raw fermented or dry cured meats may be of particular concern if destined to be used in ready-to-eat products without a further microbial reduction stage. Fermentation processes rarely deliver significant reduction in microbial pathogen levels and, as the raw materials for these products could be contaminated with organisms such as *Salmonella* and *Escherichia coli* O157, careful consideration should be given to the use of such products and especially to the controls in place at the manufacturer.

The finished products, which may be stored chilled, frozen or at ambient temperatures, depending on their inherent stability, should be assessed to ensure that the storage conditions and shelf life do not allow growth of any contaminating microorganisms.

Extensive finished product testing of products of this nature is often employed to give added assurances relating to safety, but this must not be at the expense of the adoption of hazard analysis principles.

10.3 Processing

10.3.1 Introduction

The level of processing administered to a ready meal is dictated by a number of factors, including the intended customer preparation/use, product quality and the desired shelf life. Ready meals are designed and marketed as convenience foods, many of them being sold as ready to eat or requiring only re-warming by the customer. Such products must be manufactured to prevent the entry and/or growth of microbiological hazards to ensure safety at the point of consumption. This requires an understanding of the pathogens that may be introduced by raw materials, the processing and hygienic precautions necessary to control these hazards and how they may be affected by the formulation and conditions of storage during the shelf life of the product. Ready meals containing raw ingredients, e.g. meat or poultry, that are designed for full cooking by the customer must be processed in a manner that prevents excessive levels of pathogens or their toxins from developing, which could subsequently cause illness even if the product is fully cooked.

Although safety must be the primary consideration in relation to the manufacture of these products, the presence of microorganisms capable of product spoilage is also a major factor in the processing and storage conditions applied.

10.3.2 Cooking

For short shelf life (10–14 days) refrigerated ready meals, where a heat process is applied, cooking to an internal core temperature of 70 °C for 2 minutes or equivalent is sufficient to achieve a 6 log reduction in *Listeria monocytogenes* (1). This has been advocated by the UK Department of Health (4) as the recommended cook for meat products, to achieve safety with respect to vegetative pathogens such as *Listeria monocytogenes*, assuming that recontamination does not occur after the heat process (Table 10.I).

TABLE 10.I
Equivalent heat processes required to achieve a > 6 log reduction in *Listeria monocytogenes* (4)

Temperature (°C)	Time
60	45 min
65	10 min
70	2 min
75	30 s
80	6 s

The process is also sufficient to achieve significant reductions in numbers of *E. coli* O157, i.e. greater than 6 log reduction (2), and the vast majority of *Salmonella* serotypes, including the principal strains of importance (*S. typhimurium, S. enteritidis*). This recommended process would also destroy other vegetative pathogens and most vegetative spoilage organisms capable of growing to infective or spoilage levels, respectively, within 10 days. It is not sufficient to destroy sporeforming pathogens (including psychrotrophic strains of *C. botulinum* and *B. cereus*). In addition, sporeforming spoilage bacteria, such as clostridia and bacilli, and certain thermoduric bacteria, such as micrococci or enterococci, are capable of survival and, under the right conditions, can cause spoilage.

The level of processing required must be considered in combination with product formulation. If an organism needs to grow to cause spoilage or, indeed, illness, as in the case of *B. cereus* or *S. aureus*, which must grow to high levels to produce toxin, their presence at low levels in the final product need not be cause for alarm, providing the product is formulated or stored to prevent their growth. Those pathogens capable of infection at low levels, such as *Salmonella* and *E. coli* O157, must not be present in any product that is ready to eat or where the product is not intended or likely to be fully cooked by the consumer.

Products that contain uncooked raw ingredients such as raw poultry meat, or where potential contamination may occur with *Listeria* or enteric pathogens such as *Salmonella* are usually intended to be fully cooked by the consumer. In such situations, the processing conditions must be designed to limit the level of contamination in the product and ensure that conditions do not allow the proliferation of pathogens – in particular, those capable of producing toxins that will survive the cook applied by the consumer. It is easy (but misguided) to be complacent with raw products of this nature, with a false assumption that Good Manufacturing Practices are of little importance given the fact that the consumer will ensure an effective cook. Such complacency is misplaced, as high levels of pathogens introduced as a consequence of poor raw material processing, final product control or hygiene practices present the consumer with elevated cross-contamination risks, or may even exceed the capacity of the cook to reduce the initial contamination to safe levels. Every effort must be made, even with raw products, to ensure that contamination is limited by effective manufacturing practices. Clearly, however, significant emphasis on the safety of these products is placed on the consumer cook, and guidance given on pack for such purposes is therefore very important. (See section 10.4.3.)

10.3.3 Sous vide

Sous vide is the process of cooking a product in its final packaging. Although not commonly adopted in the UK, sous vide processing is more common in

Europe. Carried out correctly, it can be used to extend the shelf life of products by destroying spoilage and pathogenic microorganisms of concern and preventing recontamination by ensuring pack integrity – the same principle as used in canning. Sous vide, in combination with refrigeration, can allow for relatively mild heat treatments to be applied (70–90 °C), which benefits product quality. However, the process must be carefully considered in conjunction with the product formulation and shelf life to ensure safety. Principal pathogens of concern in sous vide pasteurised products are psychrotrophic *C. botulinum* and *B. cereus*, unless the product has been formulated to prevent their growth. Both are capable of surviving mild heat treatments (including 70 °C for 2 minutes), and of growth at refrigeration temperatures (<8 °C).

Where a product (vacuum- or modified-atmosphere packed) will support the growth of psychrotrophic *C. botulinum*, and is allocated an extended shelf life (greater than 10 days), a minimum heat process of 90 °C for 10 minutes is recommended by the UK Advisory Committee on the Microbiological Safety of Food (5). This process will deliver a 6-log reduction of psychrotrophic *C. botulinum*, although, if the food contains lysozyme, e.g. egg white, the level of reduction may be reduced as lysozyme aids the recovery of sub-lethally heat-damaged *C. botulinum*. If stored under refrigerated conditions, however, this is not believed to be of major significance (3).

Psychrotrophic *B. cereus* is more heat-resistant than psychrotrophic *C. botulinum*, although it causes a far less severe form of illness. Although capable of psychrotrophic growth, this organism does not appear to have been associated with foodborne outbreaks or illness in properly refrigerated foods. Most incidents of *B. cereus* illness arise as a result of the product receiving some form of temperature abuse, usually involving lengthy periods at ambient temperature, although it can produce toxin after extended periods (24 days) at 4 °C (6). At present, storage at <5 °C would generally be considered to be an acceptable form of control in short-shelf-life ready meals in relation to this hazard, although storage for extended periods in sous vide products (several weeks) or at higher temperature (5–8 °C) may necessitate the adoption of a higher heat process or formulation control to restrict growth. The safety of such products may need to be validated by suitable challenge test studies conducted in experimental facilities.

10.3.4 Validation of the cooking process and process control

The variety of cooking techniques used in ready meal production is diverse, but all must be set up and monitored to ensure that the intended process is being applied consistently, if safety and stability are to be maintained from one batch to the next.

Whilst processes will vary widely, the factors that need to be considered in validating a process are often common, and a list of some of these factors is given below. It should be noted that, for individual processes, other factors may be important and may need to be considered in the validation work. Validation of process efficacy must be established prior to product launch, as part of the development process. It should be carried out for different product formulations and sizes, and if process equipment or conditions change. The key aim of process validation is to establish the process required to deliver a safe product under combined worst case process conditions, taking account of the largest size and coldest raw material placed in the coolest part of the oven, and then subjected to the minimum time/temperature conditions during the cook. The points noted in Fig. 10.2 are all important considerations that should be taken into account when establishing the efficacy of a process.

Determine if cold spots exist within the oven/vessel

Monitor product cook temperature by placing in slowest heating spot (e.g. core of product and slowest heating part of oven/vessel)

Largest piece/weight product (where applicable) used for the validation and then piece size/weight monitored in subsequent production batches

All monitoring equipment calibrated correctly and on an appropriate schedule

Ingoing temperature range of product determined and lowest temperature batch used for validation studies. Depending on how the cook is monitored, the ingoing temperature may need to be monitored as a critical control in subsequent production batches

Validation carried out using equipment under worst case loading conditions, i.e. a full load

Fig. 10.2. Key points for validation of cooking processes

The above should all be considered for normal operating conditions and do not account for operator error or breakdowns, for which other controls may need to be considered. To illustrate the above, consider the following example:

A company produces prawn balls; raw prawns are wrapped in a thin pastry, which are then steamed on racks to achieve a minimum temperature equivalent to 70 °C for 2 minutes. The steamer has been checked using data loggers and it was found that the bottom right corner closest to the steamer door heats slightly slower than the rest of the oven. The balls are manually prepared and placed onto trays, and either cooked immediately or stored in a refrigerator prior to steaming. The temperature of the balls can vary between 3 °C and 10 °C, dependent upon whether they have been in the chiller for a short time or whether they have been stored overnight. Racks can be mixed in the steamers such that overnight-stored and freshly prepared racks can be steamed together, but there is no mixing on any given rack. Because the balls are manually assembled, there can be variation in size (4.5–5 cm diameter) and weight (25–30 g).

The company chooses to monitor the core temperature of a single ball in the steamer, and uses this to determine when the cook has been achieved, at which point the cooked product is removed. Before cooking, the company checks the temperature of each rack that has been stored overnight to pick out the coldest product rack. A prawn ball representative of the upper end of the size/weight range (5 cm/30 g) is then visually selected and checked, and this is positioned in the coldest part of the oven. The probe is placed in the centre of the prawn ball, such that it pierces a prawn. The oven probe is calibrated twice annually by a specialist company, but, as the critical probe for the process, it is checked daily against hand-held probes, which are themselves calibrated daily using ice and boiling water alongside a reference thermometer. The hand-held probes are also subject to a weekly check against a reference probe at 60, 70 and 80 °C (covering the temperature range of interest). The prawn balls are then steamed.

Because each prawn ball is not weighed/sized before cooking, there may be some balls that are slightly bigger than that selected for probing. In addition, the probe may not be in the exact centre of either a prawn or the ball. To take account of this, the company has already carried out validation studies using specially prepared prawn balls of 6 cm diameter (35 g), which are exceptionally large and would represent the largest product ever expected in normal production. These take 60 seconds longer to achieve an equivalent cook of 70 °C for 2 minutes, in comparison with the average size prawn ball. This was used by the company to build a safety margin into the process, such that a cook equivalent to 70 °C for 3 minutes is achieved instead of 2. Each cook is monitored using thermograph charts, and a digital readout. The operator checks that the two readings correspond, and the chart speed is checked biannually, with a daily crosscheck using a stopwatch for the first cook of the day. Each thermograph is signed by the operator and by QC at the end of the shift before despatch.

10.3.5 Cooling

The rate of cooling of any neutral-pH, high-water-activity food product following a cooking process is critical.

Where mild heat treatments are applied (70 °C for 2 minutes or 90 °C for 10 minutes), typical of ready meal production, the principal pathogens that are of concern during cooling are sporeformers, notably *C. perfringens*, *B. cereus* and *C. botulinum* (mesophilic and, depending on the process, psychrotrophic strains). In addition, any vegetative pathogens contaminating the product after it has cooled below lethal temperatures also have an opportunity to grow. *C. perfringens* is of greatest concern. It is frequently present in raw materials such as meat, vegetables and spices, is heat-resistant (D_{100} value 0.05–17 minutes depending on strain and heating medium (7)), and is capable of growth over a wide temperature range (15–52 °C (7)). Growth is particularly rapid in the 'high ambient' range around 40 °C, where it can double approximately every 13 minutes in a neutral-pH, high-water-activity product (7) typical of many ready meals.

Note: The D value is the time required to reduce the initial level of the microorganism by 10 fold , 90% or 1 order of magnitude, i.e. a D_{100} of 1 minute would mean that at 100 °C it would take 1 minute to reduce the starting level by 10 fold.

Whilst no statutory requirements for cooling times of ready meals exist in the UK, the United States Food and Drug Administration requires cooked potentially hazardous foods to be cooled from 60 to 21 °C within 2 hours, and from 21 °C to 5 °C (or 7 °C in some instances) within a further 4 hours (8). Adoption of these guidelines would adequately control the hazard from *C. perfringens* during cooling.

As with cooking, validation of cooling should be carried out and must take account of worst case conditions, e.g. cooling in a chiller under full expected loading, under typical production conditions (chiller doors opening, etc.), and where airflow is most restricted. Multichannel dataloggers are appropriate for validating both cooking and cooling processes.

10.3.6 Storage

Storage of raw, interim or finished products demands close control to ensure both safety and quality. Finished cooked product should be maintained at refrigeration temperatures, and time spent at temperatures above 5 °C must be kept to a minimum. Any organism that has survived the cooking process, or has been introduced as a post-process contaminant can pose either a safety or a spoilage concern. Where product is subject to further processing after the cooking stage, every effort should be made to keep temperatures to a minimum and reduce time spent out of refrigeration. The effect of storage times and temperatures post-cooking on the growth of potential contaminants must be assessed and limits should be clearly documented. This must take into account the product's formulation and the subsequent shelf life that is to be assigned, and the use of predictive models provides a quick means of establishing the safety of the process.

Where storage of raw materials and in-progress material is concerned, the principal hazard is presented by organisms or their toxins that can survive the cooking process that is to follow and carry over into the finished cooked product. Toxin-producing bacteria, such as *S. aureus* and *C. perfringens*, will be controlled by effective refrigeration (<5 °C) and by minimising the time the material is exposed to non-refrigeration conditions, e.g. <2 h. Other pathogenic sporeformers, however, such as *C. botulinum* and *B. cereus*, may also grow during storage (either chilled or otherwise) and the period of storage of intermediate components needs to take account of the potential for these and other psychrotrophic organisms to increase during such stages. Certain products present specific, inherent hazards such as scombroid fish, e.g. tuna, mackerel, sardines, etc., due to the potential formation of histamine, as detailed earlier in this chapter. Appropriate controls, such as low-temperature storage (<4 °C) or shelf life restriction, must be implemented to control this hazard.

In addition to the safety considerations, growth of spoilage organisms and the development of taints will carry over into finished product.

Control is achieved through evaluating and setting maximum shelf lives on raw materials. In addition, raw materials are purchased to quality and microbiological specifications.

10.3.7 Rework

Rework is sometimes used in ready meal production, as in other food sectors, to reduce wastage. The storage and handling of rework must be controlled to ensure both the safety and quality of the finished product.

For rework that is to be re-cooked, the principal food safety concerns relate to organisms or their toxins that will survive the heat process administered, and rework storage times and temperature should restrict growth of toxin and sporeforming organisms, such as *S. aureus, C. botulinum* and *B. cereus*. In the case of ready meals containing scombroid fish such as tuna, histamine formation is an important consideration. Conditions for growth and development of these organisms are given at the end of this chapter, and predictive models/challenge testing can be used to determine safe conditions. In general, rework should be kept to a minimum and, where used, it should be chilled quickly to ≤5 °C and used rapidly (within 1–2 days, if stored chilled).

Consideration should also be given to the longer-term effects of using rework. If part of the product is continually being 'recycled', over time, this could lead to progressively higher levels of sporeformers building up in the finished product as these would be preferentially selected by the heat process. This could lead to the safety or stability of the finished product being compromised over its shelf life. The opportunity for such occurrences will be dependent upon the amount of rework added to the finished product, and how often 'break points' are scheduled, whereby, after a predetermined number of days, all remaining rework is destroyed, and there is a return to a 'virgin' batch, free from rework.

Rework should be traceable, in the same way as raw materials or in progress material, with documentation of the date of production being essential components.

10.3.8 Topping up

In the production of many ready meals, it is common practice to top up sauce/filling depositors during production. This is often a necessary practice, to ensure efficient production, but the microbiological implications should, as with other parts of the process, be considered as part of the HACCP system.

Where fresh material is continually added to old, bacterial numbers will increase in the vessel if held under temperatures supporting growth. For example, if the total bacterial count in the first batch of a sauce has the opportunity to increase by 2 log (100-fold) during depositing over 2–3 hours, and this is topped up such that the remains of the first batch account for 10% of the refilled hopper, the overall count will have increased by 1 log (10-fold), assuming complete mixing. Clearly, if this is repeated several times, bacterial levels would continue to increase to a point where the safety or quality of the product, either immediately or during its shelf life, could be compromised. In addition, if product becomes trapped in 'deadspots' within a vessel, bacterial numbers can increase without the dilution effect described above, such that higher levels are reached sooner. If these remnants of old material then rejoin the main product flow, they could result in sporadic, unevenly distributed 'hot spots' of contamination throughout a batch. This is a particular problem in pasta production, where long production runs over several days are commonplace, but the hazard of microbial proliferation applies equally to other disciplines and appropriate controls must be implemented.

As an example of the hazard presented by this practice, *C. perfringens* could increase from 1 per g to 1,000 per g in a cooked sauce with neutral pH and high water activity, within about 2.5–3 hours, if kept under warm conditions. Clearly, this would differ for different products and would depend on product formulation and storage temperature. An acidic sauce or one that was chilled and deposited from a jacketed vessel would allow longer continuous runs before a cleandown. Where HACCP identifies a potential risk, monitoring of spoilage organisms or predictive modelling of pathogenic organisms may be required to determine the correct cleaning frequency.

10.3.9 Post-process additions

Ingredients added to a ready-to-eat product without further bactericidal processing must be either previously processed to destroy pathogens of concern or be subject to stringent raw material quality assurance programmes, supported by analysis to minimise the risk of pathogens being present, and to ensure compliance with maximum levels of spoilage/indicator organisms.

Any natural ingredient that has not been subject to a bactericidal process should be considered to present a potential risk of *Listeria* contamination, and, although rarer, the further risk of *Salmonella* contamination. Herbs and spices and fruit and vegetables are frequently added after heat processing. Dipping may be employed for fresh vegetables, fruits and some herbs, using a suitable decontaminant, such as chlorine or chlorine dioxide. As with any other process, control is critical, with dwell times and dosage defined and controlled. Research has shown differences in the level of reduction achieved by dipping, depending upon product type and the organism of concern. Undoubtedly, the physical removal of organisms by washing is important, and, to prevent spread of contamination via water, a minimum chlorine level of 50–100 ppm is recommended. Washing in chlorinated water achieves at best a 2-log reduction in microorganisms and cannot be seen as a substitute for effective control by the raw material supplier.

Where dipping is not possible, and no further processing can be applied without destroying the ingredient, there is greater reliance on control at source – good agricultural practice supported by QC testing at a level that gives sufficient confidence. The sampling rate must reflect the potential hazards present in the raw material and the seriousness of the pathogen of concern. It must be remembered that microbiological testing alone provides very little assurance of safety, as the chances of detecting low numbers of pathogens that may not be evenly distributed in products are exceptionally low.

10.4 Final Product Considerations

10.4.1 Shelf life

The microbiological shelf life of ready meals can be highly variable depending on the individual product formulation but, in general, there are two key criteria that must be considered in establishing the life – firstly, the potential for growth of those pathogenic bacteria that may be present in the product and secondly the potential growth of spoilage microorganisms. The safe shelf life can only be set by understanding the microbial pathogens that may be present and assessing how they may grow in the ready meal, given the normal product formulation and the expected storage temperature. Mathematical models that predict the growth of different foodborne microorganisms are available that can estimate the growth of food-poisoning bacteria under variable conditions of pH, water activity, temperature, gaseous environment, e.g. carbon dioxide (CO_2) and preservatives such as nitrite and lactic acid. Such models can assist in identifying potentially unsafe shelf lives and help predict the formulation changes, e.g. pH reduction, that should be made to achieve a safe shelf life or, indeed, what restrictions in shelf life that could be applied to ensure safety. Mathematical models need to be used carefully by experienced individuals and, in many cases, these models should be supplemented with challenge testing of individual products in experimental facilities to determine more accurately the growth potential of key pathogens in the food.

In the vast majority of ready meals, the principal microbial pathogens of note that are capable of growth in the final product stored under good chill conditions are *L. monocytogenes* and *C. botulinum* (psychrotrophic strains). Although some strains of *B. cereus* can grow and produce toxin at 4 °C, outbreaks of foodborne illness implicating this organism have resulted almost exclusively from temperature abuse of the food, and it is not considered a major hazard in relation to growth in most ready meals that have short shelf lives (8–14 days) and where storage temperatures are generally <5 °C with short periods up to 8 °C. Products in which the organism may need closer consideration include those containing raw ingredients, where it may occur in higher numbers, such as highly spiced meals, rice/pasta dishes and dairy-based products. In such cases, control is usually exerted by regular monitoring of the raw ingredients for the organism to ensure that levels are under effective control. In addition, it may also be of concern to those products where the shelf life is extensive, e.g. sous vide, where greater potential exists for growth owing to the longer life. Under such conditions, the control options include processing to destroy the organism, formulating to prevent excessive growth or strict maintenance of low temperatures (<4 °C). This may need to be supported by challenge tests to validate the safety of the proposed shelf life of the product.

Products that are cooked in hermetically sealed containers to 90 °C for 10 minutes or equivalent are normally considered to be safe with regard to *C. botulinum* and *L. monocytogenes* and, although some strains of *B. cereus* may survive, as detailed above, such products should achieve safe shelf lives of several weeks if stored under conditions of <5 °C. As noted above, this may, however, need to be substantiated for *B. cereus* in long-shelf-life products. Products like these, i.e. cooked in pack, are often termed sous vide but it must be remembered that not all sous vide products receive a heat process of 90 °C for 10 minutes. In these cases, *L. monocytogenes* may be destroyed if the temperature exceeds 70 °C for 2 minutes but sporeforming organisms such as *C. botulinum* may remain a hazard.

Products cooked at 70 °C for 2 minutes in pack and subsequently hot-filled at >70 °C but not achieving 90 °C for 10 minutes are considered to present minimal concern with regard to *L. monocytogenes*, but spores of *C. botulinum* and *B. cereus* will survive. Shelf lives of products processed in this way should therefore be set taking account of the potential for these organisms to grow and produce toxin under the storage conditions of the product. For example, in a neutral-pH product (pH 6.5) of high water activity (0.99), *C. botulinum* is predicted to grow at 5 °C from 1 to 10^3 in 15 days (9). Reducing the pH or water activity slightly can slow down the growth of this organism. For example, reducing the pH to 6.0 would result in the predicted growth from 1 to 10^3 in 23 days at 5 °C. However, storage of the same product at higher temperatures, e.g. 8 °C, can significantly increase the speed of growth. In many cases, the shelf life of products in this category is restricted by food-spoilage bacteria, including thermotolerant species such as some lactic acid bacteria, clostridia and even sporeforming moulds and yeasts. In these and, indeed, the previous category of products, i.e. products heated to 90 °C for 10 minutes, it must be remembered that any contaminants left in the product have very little microbial competition as the process eliminates most other microorganisms. Therefore, growth of contaminating or surviving spoilage and pathogenic microorganisms will often be unchallenged.

Nevertheless, these products, because they exclude the presence of many post-process contaminants, can achieve fairly long shelf lives at 5 °C or below (10–14 days).

For products that are cold-mixed or filled at temperatures below 70 °C, *L. monocytogenes, C. botulinum* and *B. cereus* may all be present in the finished product and need to be controlled. Under such circumstances, the shelf life is usually restricted to <10 days at 5 °C or below unless individual product parameters, e.g. pH, a_w, etc., are shown to restrict the growth of the contaminating pathogens using mathematical models or challenge tests in experimental facilities. It should also be remembered that such products will allow the survival of any other contaminating pathogens such as *S. aureus, Salmonella*, etc., that may have been introduced from the raw ingredients or through handling or processing. Such organisms will not generally grow at low temperatures, e.g. <8 °C, but refrigeration will have no effect on their survival. As well as the potential for foodborne pathogens, ready meals that are not hot-filled carry a fairly high loading of general microflora from the component ingredients, equipment and general handling. Yeasts and moulds, Enterobacteriaceae, lactic acid bacteria and pseudomonads predominate, although sporeforming microorganisms can be high in some products, particularly highly spiced meals. The ingredients, formulation and storage conditions play a significant role in the nature of the spoilage that the product succumbs to. Neutral, proteinaceous foods tend to be spoiled by pseudomonads, with the production of objectionable off-odours apparent at time intervals dependent on the temperature of storage and, to some degree, by the strength of flavour of the product.

Typical shelf lives allocated to ready meals are shown in Table 10.II.

TABLE 10.II
Some typical shelf lives allocated to ready meals

Product category	Principal microbial hazards	Quality shelf life (days)	Safe shelf life (days)[a]
Raw, to be cooked	Enteric pathogens (if improperly cooked), *C. botulinum*	6-8	14[b]
Cold mix, ready to eat	*C. botulinum, B. cereus* and *L. monocytogenes*	8-10	10 or less
Cooked in pack (>90 °C, 10 min), ready to eat	*C. botulinum* and *B. cereus*	14-21	*ca* 21[c]
Cooked (in pack or hot fill >70 °C), ready to eat	*C. botulinum* and *B. cereus*	10-15	14[b]
Cooked, non hot fill, ready to eat	*C. botulinum, B. cereus* and *L. monocytogenes*	8-10	10 or less

[a] Assuming neutral (pH 6.5-7.0), high water activity (a_w 0.99) products stored at 5 °C or lower.

[b] The Advisory Committee on the Microbiological Safety of Food (ACMSF) recommends that products stored under vacuum or modified atmospheres should have a shelf life of 10 days or less at ≤5 °C (5).

[c] Growth of surviving spores of *B. cereus* may need assessing using challenge tests.

The shelf lives given in this table are for guidance purposes only. It is recommended that a full hazard analysis be conducted on each product to determine the hazards and appropriate shelf life.

Products with large amounts of fermentable carbohydrates, such as sucrose and lactose, often succumb to more visual spoilage caused by the growth and gas production by yeasts and sometimes Enterobacteriaceae. Both of these organisms grow quickly and can produce copious quantities of gas, causing blowing of the pack. Low-pH products restrict the growth of pseudomonads and Enterobacteriaceae, and spoilage tends to occur as a result of the growth of yeasts, although a high proportion of spoilage in these and many other ready meals is caused by mould. Mould spoilage can develop from single spores and, although growth is relatively slow in the low concentrations of oxygen available and at low temperatures, they can scavenge low oxygen levels sufficient to form visible colonies on the food – such a colony being readily visible to the eye and most often greeted by product rejection. Although less frequently, ready meals can be spoilt by lactic acid bacterial growth in longer-shelf-life products with the production of acid and sickly sweet taints. In very deteriorated products, lactic acid bacteria and other organisms, particularly pseudomonads, can produce visible slime on products, but levels will usually be exceptionally high ($>10^8$/g) at the point where this occurs.

Microbiological quality is best determined by means of simple storage trials with determination of microbial growth during the life. Although it is possible to make some judgement regarding shelf life using microbial counts, it is best assessed in conjunction with organoleptic assessment of the product. Shelf life determination should be conducted under conditions that simulate those experienced by the product. Ideally, this should be done using production samples, packed and stored under the same conditions intended for the final product. Product should be stored at temperatures simulating those experienced through manufacture, distribution, retail and with the customer. Although never likely to be absolutely accurate, storage at 5–8 °C gives a good reflection of the durability of the ready meal under normal conditions.

Others have found it equally suitable to store product under regimes of variable temperature, such as 2–4 °C for periods from manufacture and through distribution, 4–6 °C for retail storage and 8–10 °C for customer storage, with a short period at ambient temperatures (2–4 h) to simulate customer usage after purchase. It is not possible to obtain a perfect shelf life test that simulates all conditions, but using the above strategies has proved to be adequate.

Microorganisms to be tested should include all those expected to be present or capable of causing spoilage in the final products. This usually includes a basic aerobic plate count, together with yeast and mould, Enterobacteriaceae, *S. aureus, E. coli, B. cereus, Salmonella* and *Listeria.* Tests may also be supplemented with *C. perfringens* for highly spiced and meat-containing products, where its presence may occasionally be expected. High levels of aerobic plate count (APC), particularly at the start of life, should be investigated to determine the nature of the organisms.

Shelf life can be extended by storage under modified atmospheres using carbon dioxide and nitrogen or by the addition of preservative factors. Increased salt concentration will restrict the growth of many spoilage bacteria, as will the presence of additional organic acids, e.g. acetic, lactic, citric, etc., although these are most effective at lower pH (<5.5). Preservatives such as benzoate and sorbate can restrict the growth of moulds and achieve longer open life, although it should be remembered that moulds are best controlled by effective hygiene and environmental cleaning programmes in the filling area.

oked ingredient life

Ready meals, in their simplest form, may be prepared from raw ingredients, cooked, packed, chilled and despatched for sale. However, owing to the nature of large-scale manufacture, a variety of components in some ready meals may be manufactured separately, and these are chilled and stored for subsequent final product assembly, often 1–3 days later. For example, a typical lasagne will be made using freshly cooked pasta to which previously cooked, chilled and stored white sauce and meat filling will be added. The safety criteria for these pre-manufactured components destined to be cold/warm-filled is as critical as the manufacture of the ready meal itself. Cooking and cooling times to destroy and prevent growth of pathogens, respectively, must be adhered to. As these products may be stored for several days prior to use, the potential growth of contaminating pathogens and spoilage microorganisms must be considered from the point of manufacture of the component to the end of life of the final product, unless the components will be re-cooked as part of the production process. Therefore, if it is considered that a total life of a ready meal should be restricted to 10 days because of the potential for contamination and growth of *Listeria*, then the life starts at the point at which any ingredient may itself be prone to contamination by the organism and not from the point of final packing. Thus, if a perishable ingredient or component can be stored for a period of 2 days prior to final assembly and it is exposed to environmental contamination, then the life of the packed finished product should not exceed 8 days from make-up. The nature of the hazard associated with sub recipe ingredients must therefore be taken into account when establishing the safe lives of the final products.

10.4.3 On-pack labelling (usage and cooking instructions)

An important component of the safety of ready meals is the customer use of instructions or on-pack labelling.

The labelling must give clear guidance to the customer about the required storage, durability and preparation requirements for the product. As chilled meals are usually highly perishable, most ready meals give clear instructions to 'Store Refrigerated', whilst some also specify maximum temperatures, e.g. 'Store at <5 °C'. The durability indicator on the product is usually the 'Use By' date, which should be applied to any food that may become unsafe to consume after this date. In practice, the shelf-life-limiting factor is often microbial spoilage and the shelf life of a ready meal is restricted for this reason rather than for reasons of safety. Nevertheless, as the storage and durability indicators are so important, it is essential that they are bold, large and clear and on the front of the pack.

Prepared meals may be presented to the customer as ready-to-eat, where the customer may consume it with little or no re-cooking, i.e. cold or mild heating, or they may be presented as ready-to-cook (or stir-fry/microwave), where the subsequent heat process is designed to destroy pathogenic bacteria that may be present in the product.

Irrespective of the intended preparation of the product, the packaging usually depicts the prepared/cooked product on the front. It is therefore possible for people to confuse raw products for cooked products and, whilst this should be apparent on opening those products containing raw meats and poultry, it may not be so readily obvious for partially cooked or enrobed products, i.e. flash-fried, crumbed chicken, etc. It is therefore essential that the preparation/cooking requirements of the product are presented clearly on the pack.

Cooking instructions need to be generated with due consideration to the large number of factors that influence whether the product will be cooked effectively and include the following: ingoing temperature of the product (the time to cook a chilled food with initial temperature of 8 °C may be less than for one starting at 0–2 °C) and the size of the product (cooking times will differ markedly if poor control exists over piece or portion size). Other important factors include the distance from the heat source (for grilled products), the number of products being cooked simultaneously (particularly important when microwaving), the nature of the heat source (gas and electric grills can differ markedly, whilst different power settings on a microwave can dramatically affect heating and cooking), turning frequency (more frequent turning of grilled, oven-cooked or even fried products can enhance heating, but this must be balanced against convenience) and duration of the cook. All of these factors must be taken into account when generating a cooking instruction for products and must be clearly defined on the pack. Where the product must be cooked to destroy pathogenic microorganisms, i.e. raw ready meals, then the instruction given must achieve a minimum of 70 °C for 2 minutes or equivalent, throughout the product. In practice, when generating instructions, it is normal to build in significant margins of safety, e.g. 75–80 °C, to account for the large variation in cooking methods and appliances in the home. Indeed, it is often of equal importance to give additional qualitative indicators of cooking efficacy on pack, such as: 'Ensure the product is piping hot before serving' as an extra safeguard.

10.5 Hygiene

10.5.1 Cleaning

Effective cleaning is essential to prevent build-up of product residues and the development of microorganisms on surfaces, which could lead to cross-contamination. *Listeria* is the principal organism of concern in ready-to-eat products where site hygiene is concerned, although poor hygiene can lead to colonisation and build-up of a range of microorganisms, which may compromise both the stability and the safety of the product.

Cleaning, as with other processes critical to product safety and quality, should be scheduled according to a risk assessment of the operation. The frequency of cleaning must take account of pathogens that may be present in the product or on the component and, given their growth characteristics, determine how quickly, and to what levels they may grow between scheduled cleans, should they be present. As an example, *S. aureus* is a frequent contaminant in raw meat. In operations where raw meat is bowl-chopped prior to cooking, *S. aureus* growth to high levels is a potential concern, due to the heat resistance of its toxin, which will survive most cooking processes. Control must therefore be aimed at controlling growth in the raw meat and on associated equipment. Refrigeration will effectively control its growth, which will not occur below 10 °C, but the heat generated during bowl chopping can permit growth, and, if left for sufficient time, toxin may be produced. The cleaning frequency must therefore be established taking into account such hazards. The use of microbiological testing to monitor build-up of contamination over time, in order to establish appropriate cleaning frequency, can be useful.

In choosing cleaning chemicals, advice should be sought from the chemicals supplier as to the most appropriate detergents and disinfectants for a particular application. Product residues can effectively protect many bacteria from disinfectants, either by neutralising the active form of the disinfectant or by physically 'shielding' the organism from contact with the chemical. Cleaning usually involves at least three stages: physical removal of product residues, use of a detergent to break down fat, followed by a disinfection cycle. The build-up of protein or salt deposits (scale) on some equipment can precede biofilm development, and occasional acid cleaning may be necessary to remove such deposits. Whichever chemicals are chosen, their effectiveness in the factory should be verified through monitoring of cleaning efficacy.

To ensure that hygiene is maintained throughout the entire site, it is best practice to draw up a cleaning schedule. This should list each part of the factory – floors, walls and equipment – and a cleaning frequency based on potential build-up of 'soil' and microorganisms should be established, such that everything is cleaned over a defined time period. (See Chapter 4.)

Monitoring cleaned surfaces using an aerobic plate count (APC), or adenosine tri-phosphate (ATP) kits, can be used to highlight deficiencies that could be due to inadequate cleaning by the staff involved, the incorrect use of cleaning chemicals (e.g. dosing), or equipment that is not designed hygienically (see section 10.6.3).

One of the main areas that can compromise the safety and quality of ready meals is ineffective cleaning, leading to build-up of microbial contaminants, and transfer to intermediate or finished products. In the vast majority of cases, doing the simple things properly, such as ensuring that all product residues are removed during cleaning are the key foundation for safe, high-quality products.

*10.5.2 High/low risk**

Physical and procedural separation of raw unprocessed materials and processed finished product is now industry standard. Although on a small scale it is possible to safely process food in a common area (as we do in our kitchens daily), the scale of most commercial operations, with large workforces, makes it very difficult to rely upon procedures alone to prevent cross-contamination from raw to finished product. The introduction of physical barriers goes much of the way towards reducing this risk of contamination, but cannot alone eliminate cross-contamination if other routes are not controlled; factories with good physical separation have been involved in food poisoning incidents, where they have failed to recognise other routes of contamination.

Meat is a common ingredient in ready meals manufacture and presents, without exception, the highest risk of any raw material with respect to pathogen cross-contamination to the finished product. The incidence of *Salmonella*, *E. coli* O157, and *Campylobacter* in meats and poultry is shown in Table 10.III.

TABLE 10.III
Incidence of enteric pathogens in raw meat and poultry

Product	Organism incidence (%)		
	Salmonella	***E. coli* O157**	***Campylobacter***
Beef	0-5	0-4	0-5
Lamb	0-5	0-2	0-10
Poultry	0-30	0-1	20-100
Pork	0-10	0-2	0-20

As pathogens such as *Salmonella* and *E. coli* O157 can cause illness at very low levels, their mere presence in food often leads to rejection, withdrawal and possibly recall of product from the shelf. Handling raw and cooked meat at a commercial production site demands the very highest level of high/low-risk separation. The level of separation required in practice is very much based on risk assessment, and will depend on many factors, but

---

* High risk in this text refers to the cooked side of an operation, often also called high care. Low risk refers to the raw, unprocessed area.

..rgely determined by the level of risk presented by the raw materials handled, and the degree of exposure of the processed product.

The principal cross-contamination routes are equipment, people, water and air. More detailed guidance can be found in other texts (10) and in Chapter 4.

10.6 Microbiological Testing and Specifications

Microbiological testing of raw ingredients, in-process materials and finished product, together with the environment and equipment, are extremely important elements in product safety and quality assurance programmes.

Compliance with defined microbiological criteria is often required as part of a purchase agreement between a manufacturer and a purchaser, most often a retailer. These requirements are detailed in a microbiological specification and it is essential that, before agreeing such specifications, both parties understand the implications of the specification in terms of the microorganism specified, target/unacceptable levels, frequency of testing and action to be taken in the event of the criterion being exceeded.

Careful consideration must be given to developing strategies for the use of microbiological testing in order to provide useful information about the microbial integrity of the entire production process. This is usually defined in a sampling plan, which is best broken down into four key areas; raw materials, process, end product and environment.

10.6.1 Raw materials

Raw materials should be subject to routine screening for microorganisms. The choice of test and frequency will be dependent on the degree of risk the material represents and the associated supplier assurance programme. Whilst many ingredients, such as cooked meat, herbs and spices, pasteurised dairy material, etc., may be subject to supplier analysis for indicators of quality (APC), hygiene (Enterobacteriaceae) and pathogens (*Salmonella* and *Listeria*), such tests should be supplemented with regular intake testing by the manufacturer as verification checks. In many cases, a simple verification check could include APC and *E. coli* to give added assurance that the material has not been abused. The testing frequency, organism and limits should be documented as part of a sampling plan for the raw ingredients.

High-risk ingredients such as herbs and spices, cooked meat, nuts, flavourings, etc., and other materials should be routinely analysed for indicators of microbial quality and safety. This would routinely include tests for APC, *E. coli, Salmonella* and possibly *Listeria*. In general, *E. coli* levels should be <10/g and both *L. monocytogenes* and *Salmonella* would be expected to be not detectable in 25-g samples.

10.6.2 Environmental sampling

Environmental sampling plans should be focused to determine two key issues: where contamination may be occurring/building up and, secondly, the efficacy of cleaning programmes to eliminate such contamination.

Assessing cleaning efficacy is achieved in three ways: visually inspecting after cleaning, microbiological testing, or determination of product/microbial residues by ATP measurement.

Microbiological testing will usually include monitoring for APC or coliforms/Enterobacteriaceae in the environment, supplemented by monitoring for *Listeria* species. A sampling plan should be developed based on the factory and equipment layout, and sampling points should be established by 'walking the plant' to visually assess areas that may lead to build-up of microbial contaminants. Clearly, such areas should ideally be designed out of the plant. Areas naturally difficult to clean effectively, such as tanks, mixing vessels and slicers, should be routinely included. Typical areas where *Listeria* may build up, together with strategies for its control, have been detailed more thoroughly in other texts (1) and a summary of these is given in Table 10.IV.

Assessing cleaning efficacy is perhaps best achieved these days using more rapid indicators of hygiene, such as ATP measurement, which allow the instant assessment of cleaning as they detect both product and microbial residues left on the plant after cleaning, both of which may indicate inadequately cleaned surfaces.

No matter what test is applied, it is important to establish levels that indicate effective cleaning and those that demonstrate inadequacies. Exact figures to aim for are difficult to document for all different production plants but, after cleaning of high-risk areas in ready meal factories, the coliforms/Enterobacteriaceae levels should generally achieve <10 per swab (where a swab is taken from an area of approximately 10 cm x 10 cm).

Many companies, as well as using swabs, also monitor the rinse water from the CIP (cleaning in place) system as an indicator of effective cleaning. It is extremely important to recognise, however, that a result from any swab or rinse is dependent on sampling the place where contamination is residing, together with the technique used for swabbing, subsequent storage of the swab and the method used for analysis.

Swabs for microbial detection should be pre-moistened using recovery diluent and, if swabbing a surface where terminal sanitisers may be present, then appropriate neutraliser needs to be incorporated, such as lecithin/Tween 80 for quaternary ammonium compounds and sodium thiosulfate for chlorine (11). Consideration must be given to the size of the swab in relation to the size of the area being swabbed, with swabs for *Listeria* spp often needing to cover larger areas such as floors, walls and equipment surfaces and therefore necessitating larger sponge swabs. Cotton-tipped swabs are not suitable for swabbing such large areas and should be restricted for the use of swabbing smaller areas for indicator organisms such as APC and coliforms.

TABLE 10.IV
Examples of environmental areas prone to contamination with *Listeria* species

Area	Problems
Floors	Damaged areas that can act as traps/reservoirs for debris and water (ponding) allowing *Listeria* spp to multiply.
Drains	Damaged areas that can act as traps/reservoirs for *Listeria* spp. Product debris trapped under drain cover. Overflow/blocked drain leading to excess contaminated water flooding the production environment.
Ceilings, walls and overheads, e.g. pipes, ducts and gantries.	Damaged areas that can act as traps for debris and bacteria and sources of contamination to the production environment.
Cleaning equipment, e.g. brushes, vacuum cleaners, mops, squeegees, buckets.	Contamination build-up leading to sources of high numbers of *Listeria* spp. Aerosol spread of *Listeria* spp. by use of hoses.
Floor contact items, e.g. trolley wheels, racks, bins.	Assist the spread of water and bacteria through the production environment.
Non-routine equipment, e.g. ladders, engineers equipment.	Import contamination from external areas.
Floor-contact surfaces	Cross contamination potential.
Refrigeration units	Accumulation and dissemination of *Listeria* spp via the moist air blown through the units and condensation drip from pipework.
Air handling systems, e.g. ventilation, extraction systems and air conditioning.	Accumulation and dissemination of *Listeria* spp.
Equipment and tray washing.	Inadequate cleaning leading to cross-contamination. Cross contamination of cleaned equipment from dirty equipment. Aerosols created during washing.
Personnel	Product contamination by inadequate hygiene and production practices.
Cleaning procedures	Inadequate for destroying *Listeria* spp.

Adapted from (1)

In addition, it is essential to recognise that the time between sampling the surface and analysis of the swab may also be critical to achieving an accurate result. Swabs may not support the target organism for long periods, whilst other organisms may actually grow if conditions are suitable and it is important to control the time and temperature conditions of storage prior to analysis (ideally <2 h if unrefrigerated and within 24 h if refrigerated or kept cold with ice packs). Swabs for the determination of *Listeria* or other microbial pathogens that are analysed at sub-contract facilities are often not analysed for periods up to 24 h and it is essential that the ability of the swab to support the survival of low numbers of the target organism under such conditions is validated; otherwise, all results may actually be invalid and provide no data for the factory to act upon. The aim of a swabbing programme should be to find the target organism.

Listeria is an organism that necessitates extensive routine monitoring in the production environment to ensure that it is effectively controlled. Areas requiring particular attention include product contact surfaces such as conveyors and slicing and mixing equipment, together with utensils such as knives, etc. Attention should also be given to personal clothing and also to areas coming into contact with hands, such as door handles and table ledges.

An area often overlooked in monitoring (and cleaning) are the cleaning utensils themselves, such as brushes, brush handles, spray bottle handles, clothes and hoses, all of which may build up contamination if not effectively cleaned.

A swabbing programme should be in place with clearly defined sampling points, and such programmes should be flexible to encourage hygiene personnel to include additional swab sites as they 'walk the plant'.

10.6.3 End product

Microbiological specifications for products should clearly define the level expected of the product or raw material and the level at which the microorganism becomes unacceptable. A range of specifications for microbiological testing of products is available from the Institute of Food Science and Technology (12), whilst those most often used by local authorities are detailed in the Public Health Laboratory Service guidelines for ready to eat foods (13).

The end product specification should take account of the processing included in the product. Products cooked in pack or hot-filled would be expected to have minimal post process contaminants, and therefore indicators of hygiene and processing efficacy, such as Enterobacteriaceae or coliforms, could suffice and should really achieve levels below 10/g. This may be supplemented with APC tests as a general indicator of product quality. Products that are cold-mixed or extensively handled are prone to more post-process contamination, and levels of APC or Enterobacteriaceae will be higher. An APC range of <100/g–10,000/g is not unusual for these products at the point of production and, although present,

Enterobacteriaceae should generally not exceed levels of 100/g. Products that are prone to more post-process contamination are supplemented with tests for specific pathogens, such as *Listeria* and *S. aureus*, and indicators of quality, such as yeast and mould. It is also common to test these ready meals for enteric pathogens such as *Salmonella*, although the frequency of this test varies depending on the risk it presents.

It should be remembered that many ingredients in ready meals contain starter microorganisms, e.g. salami (lactic acid bacteria and staphylococci) and cheeses (lactic acid bacteria and sometimes moulds) and it is therefore not appropriate to monitor for APC or yeasts and moulds in such foods, if the ingredients are not subject to a full cook as part of the process.

Examples of microbiological expectations for ready meals are shown in Table 10.V.

TABLE 10.V

Examples of microbiological specifications and expected results for a variety of ready meals

Ready meal type	**Microbiological expectations***		
	Microorganism	**Start of life (log cfu/g)**	**End of life (log cfu/g)**
Raw, to be cooked	APC	$<1x10^5-1x10^6$	$1x10^7-<1x10^8$
	Enterobacteriaceae	$<1x10^2-1x10^4$	$<1x10^3-1x10^5$
	Yeast and mould	$<1x10^2-1x10^4$	$<1x10^3-1x10^5$
	E. coli	$<10-1x10^2$	$<10-1x10^2$
Cold mix, ready to eat	APC	$<1x10^2-1x10^4$	$1x10^6-<1x10^7$
	Enterobacteriaceae	$<1x10^2-1x10^3$	$<1x10^2-1x10^4$
	Yeast and mould	$<10-1x10^2$	$<1x10^2-1x10^4$
	E. coli	<10	<10
	S. aureus	$<10-1x10^2$	$<10-1x10^2$
	L. monocytogenes	Not detected/25 g	Not detected/25 g
	Salmonella	Not detected/25 g	Not detected/25 g
Cooked in pack (>90 °C, 10 min), ready to eat	APC	$<1x10^2$	$1x10^3-<1x10^6$
	Enterobacteriaceae	<10	<10
Cooked (in pack or hot fill >70 °C), ready to eat	APC	$<1x10^2-1x10^3$	$1x10^3-<1x10^6$
	Enterobacteriaceae	<10	$<1x10^2$
Cooked, non-hot-fill, ready to eat	APC	$<1x10^2-1x10^4$	$1x10^6-<1x10^7$
	Enterobacteriaceae	$<1x10^2$	$<1x10^2-1x10^4$
	Yeast and mould	$<10-1x10^2$	$<1x10^2<1x10^4$
	E. coli	<10	<10
	S. aureus	$<10-1x10^2$	$<10-1x10^2$
	L. monocytogenes	Not detected/25 g	Not detected/25 g
	Salmonella	Not detected/25 g	Not detected/25 g

* The microorganism and figures given are for guidance only and microbiological criteria must be established for each individual product, taking account of raw ingredients and processing factors specific to that product.

10.7 Microorganisms

There is a diverse range of microbial groups that represent a hazard to ready meals, dictated principally by the raw materials, processing conditions and post-process hygiene. This section aims to give a brief description of the key organisms of significance to ready meal manufacturers, their sources and factors affecting their growth and survival.

10.7.1 Clostridium botulinum

This organism causes the disease botulism, the symptoms of which occur approximately 12–36 h after consumption of a food in which the organism has grown and produced its toxin. Symptoms include vomiting, drying of the mouth, difficulty in speaking and blurred vision, leading to paralysis and respiratory failure. The organism occurs in the general environment, particularly in soil and water sediments and therefore will be present in most food raw materials from time to time, albeit generally at low levels (<1/kg). It produces heat-resistant spores, which readily survive normal pasteurisation temperatures e.g. 70 °C for 2 minutes. There are two main groups of *C. botulinum* – those that cannot grow at chill temperatures below 10 °C (mesophilic), and those that grow in foods to temperatures as low as 3.3 °C (psychrotrophic); clearly, the latter present the greatest hazard to chilled ready meals. The mesophilic strains are destroyed by temperatures of 121 °C for 3 minutes (this gives >12 log reduction in spores), whereas the psychrotrophic strains are destroyed by lower temperatures of 90 °C for 10 minutes (6 log reduction). The pH required to prevent growth in foods is ≤4.6 and ≤5.0 for mesophilic and psychrotrophic strains, respectively, whilst water activity levels of ≤0.94 (or ≥10% aqueous salt) and ≤0.97 (or ≥5% aqueous salt) will prevent the growth of these respective organisms. In a neutral-pH (6.5), high-a_w (0.99) product, *C. botulinum* is predicted to grow from 1 to 10^3 within 15 days at 5 °C and 6 days at 8 °C (9). *C. botulinum* grows best under anaerobic conditions (without oxygen) but it may also grow in many foods in the presence of oxygen, as the conditions within the food are often suitable for anaerobic growth irrespective of the gaseous atmospheres. The Advisory Committee on the Microbiological Safety of Food (5) recommended that any chilled food stored under vacuum or modified-atmosphere packaging should have a chilled shelf life at ≤5 °C restricted to 10 days or less unless conditions in the food could demonstrably prevent the growth of psychrotrophic strains of *C. botulinum*.

10.7.2 Listeria monocytogenes

Listeria monocytogenes is the principal human pathogen of the *Listeria* genus. It causes listeriosis when consumed in high numbers (usually >10^3/g) by susceptible individuals. Classical listeriosis most often affects pregnant women, the young, the elderly and immunocompromised individuals with flu-like symptoms after approximately 1 day to several weeks, which may progress to meningitis, sometimes resulting in death or abortion. Consumption of extremely high levels of *L. monocytogenes* (>10^7/g) may also result in more typical food-poisoning symptoms, including vomiting and diarrhoea after 18-24 hours, with no further complications. *L. monocytogenes* can be found in soil, water and vegetation, and appears widely distributed in the general environment. It has been found in almost all food commodity types, including vegetables, meat, fish and dairy products, and it should be considered a hazard to most food raw ingredients. It readily colonises factory environments in drains and floor cracks, and its principal route into food is via contaminated raw ingredients or through cross-contamination via the environment through poor cleaning practices. It is destroyed by normal pasteurisation temperatures (70 °C for 2 minutes) and can grow at chill temperatures marginally below freezing (*ca* –0.4 °C). It does not grow in foods with a pH below approximately pH 4.4 or a_w of <0.92. In a neutral product (pH 6.5) with a high a_w (0.99), one cell is predicted to grow to >10^3 in approximately 10 days at 5 °C (9) and it can grow both aerobically and anaerobically. Control of *L. monocytogenes* in the raw material and environment is an essential element in any strategy to keep this organism out of ready meals.

10.7.3 **E. coli**

E. coli represents a group of organisms found in the intestines of humans and other warm-blooded animals. They consist of a large group of different types, most being harmless, but some of which can cause human illness. The most severe group causing foodborne outbreaks in developed countries are the verocytotoxin-producing strains of *E. coli* (VTEC), of which *E. coli* O157 is the most common type in the UK causing foodborne illness. Illness caused by *E. coli* O157 requires the ingestion of very low numbers (<100 cells), with symptoms of severe abdominal pain and diarrhoea occurring 1–6 days after consumption of the organism. This can be followed by a severe infection of the intestine, with the organism invading the tissues and causing bloody diarrhoea, which may progress to wider disruption of organ systems such as the kidney (haemolytic uraemic syndrome, HUS). In some cases, kidney failure and death may occur.

E. coli (the group) are found in the intestines of healthy humans and other animals, and the presence of the organism in food is an indication of poor standards of hygienic control. Its presence in water and primary agricultural products such as raw meat gives an indication of potential faecal cross-contamination but, as it can colonise factory environments, its presence in processed foods is usually an indication of post-process contamination from the factory environment.

Pathogenic strains of *E. coli*, such as *E. coli* O157, can be carried by humans and passed from person to person during infection, but *E. coli* O157 is more commonly associated with bovine animals (dairy cows and beef cattle) and it gains access to foods via poor standards of animal husbandry and abattoir processing, which allow faeces to contaminate the milk of cows or the meat from cattle, respectively. Additionally, it can contaminate fruit, salads and vegetables as a result of poor agricultural controls through the poor control of animal manure or through inadequate control of grazing animals. Contaminated water supplies have also caused outbreaks, and other animal species, such as sheep, can also carry the organism.

E. coli are readily destroyed by pasteurisation temperatures (70 °C for 2 minutes) and do not grow under chilled conditions (minimum < *ca* 8 °C). Although they cannot grow at low pH (< *ca* 4.4) under chilled storage, some strains of *E. coli* O157 can survive for several weeks in acid foods, e.g. fruit juice (pH <4.0), at low temperatures, and there are even reports of growth in fruit juice (pH 4.0) if stored at ambient temperature. They are inhibited by fairly low a_w (< *ca* 0.95) but, as they often cause infection from very low numbers, their mere presence and not growth is a major concern to ready to eat foods.

10.7.4 Salmonella *spp*

There are over 1,800 different types of *Salmonella*, most of which are capable of causing human illness. Typical salmonellosis occurs 12–72 hours after consuming food contaminated with the organism (<100 cells can cause infection in some foods, especially high-fat products such as chocolate) with symptoms of vomiting, diarrhoea and fever, which is usually self resolving in 1–5 days. More severe infection can occur from types such as *Salmonella typhi* and *paratyphi*, which cause more debilitating, long-term illness, but this is less common in developed countries, and is most frequently associated with holiday makers returning from the continents of Asia and Africa. *Salmonella* can be carried asymptomatically for long periods by humans, and food can become contaminated from infected food handlers. The organism infects a large number of other animal species, including chickens, cows and pigs, and readily gains access to food products such as poultry meat, eggs, raw milk and pork. The organism can also be spread by birds, flies and vermin, and pest control is an important element in controlling this organism. *Salmonella* is readily destroyed by pasteurisation temperatures (70 °C for 2 minutes) and, although there is significant variation, most types will not grow under chilled conditions (< *ca* 7 °C). Like *E. coli*, they can survive for long periods in acid foods, although growth of most strains will be prevented at pH <4.5. It grows at a_w > *ca* 0.94, but can survive for many months and years in low-a_w, dry foods such as milk powder and chocolate.

10.7.5 Staphylococcus aureus

Staphylococcus aureus is commonly associated with the human body, particularly moist areas such as the nose, throat and arms pits. It produces a large array of toxins, one of which causes the typical food poisoning of staphylococcal intoxication. Symptoms include rapid onset of vomiting (1–8 hours), sometimes accompanied by diarrhoea, and this is usually self-resolving within 1 day. Growth of the organism needs to occur to high levels in the food (>10^4–10^6/g) before sufficient toxin is produced to cause illness and, because the toxin is very heat-resistant, mild pasteurisation temperatures (70 °C) that destroy the organism will not affect the toxin, which will remain active. The organism can colonise the skin of humans and cause infections in cuts and sores, and is also associated with boils. The principal route of contamination is therefore from personnel handling practices and from people to food, although it can also be a contaminant on many raw materials, particularly meat. *S. aureus* cannot grow under chilled conditions (<10 °C) and is inhibited by pH values of <4. It can, however, tolerate very low a_w and produces enterotoxin at a_w 0.86 if other conditions are optimal.

10.7.6 Bacillus cereus

Bacillus cereus is a sporeforming bacterium that occurs in soil and dust. It causes illness by the production of toxin in food if it is allowed to grow to high levels (>10^5–10^6/g). One of two toxins is produced by the organism – an emetic toxin, which causes rapid vomiting with occasional diarrhoea 1–5 hours after consumption, and a diarrhoeal toxin, which principally causes diarrhoea with occasional nausea and vomiting, 8–16 hours after consumption. Both illnesses are usually self-limiting after approximately 1 day. Emetic illness is more commonly associated with rice- and starch-based dishes, whereas diarrhoeal illness tends to be more closely associated with meat, vegetable and highly spiced products, such as stews, soups and sauces. *B. cereus* produces heat-resistant spores that survive normal pasteurisation temperatures and are destroyed only by long periods above boiling temperatures (10–60 minutes at 100 °C will give approximately 6 log reduction), although this will vary significantly with different strains and may be much longer in low water activity foods. The emetic toxin is heat-stable and, although the diarrhoeal toxin may be destroyed by effective cooking, this should never be relied upon to make a manufactured product safe. The organism occurs in soil and dust in the general environment and is particularly associated with dried foods such as herbs and spices, but is found in most other raw materials, such as vegetables, meats and dairy products. Some strains of *B. cereus* can grow at chill temperatures, although growth is slow (toxin production has been reported after 24 days at 4 °C (6)). They do not grow at very low pH values (minimum *ca* 4.4), although they can tolerate quite dry conditions and therefore grow at fairly low a_w (minimum *ca* 0.91). In a neutral-pH food (pH 6.5) of high a_w (0.99), one cell is predicted to multiply to 10^3 at 5 °C within 11 days (9). Under chilled conditions, *B. cereus* appears to be of greatest concern to dairy foods, where it can also cause overt spoilage. The organism grows best under aerobic conditions, but many packaged foods and ready meals will support its growth. In addition to *B. cereus*, other *Bacillus* species are also implicated as foodborne pathogens if present in foods at very high levels (>10^6/g). Such organisms include *B. subtilis, B. licheniformis* and *B. pumilis*. High levels of bacilli in foods should always be investigated and identified.

10.7.7 Clostridium perfringens

Clostridium perfringens is another sporeforming bacterium that causes illness after consumption of high numbers of the organism (>10^5–10^6/g). Symptoms most often include diarrhoea, 8–22 hours after consumption, and occasionally nausea and vomiting. The illness is usually self-limiting. The organism is carried in the intestine of healthy humans and other animals and is therefore associated with animal and human faeces and the soil, and is of primary significance to raw meats and vegetables. *C. perfringens* is resistant to normal pasteurisation temperatures and is only destroyed by boiling temperatures of 100 °C for up to 1 hour or more (3–>6 log reduction). Under optimal growth conditions, *C. perfringens* is one of the fastest multiplying microbial pathogens and, as it survives cooking, it is the principal hazard during cooling of cooked products or, indeed, if cooked products are held under warm conditions. It is also capable of growth at extremely high temperatures – up to 52 °C. *C. perfringens* does not grow under chill storage (minimum 15 °C) or at low pH (minimum pH 5) or low a_w (minimum *ca* 0.95), and grows principally under anaerobic conditions, particularly relishing conditions in cooked meats. As it can grow at such high temperatures and also multiplies rapidly at warm temperatures, its growth must be restricted by holding cooked foods at high temperatures (>60 °C) or cooling them rapidly, usually to <5 °C in 4 hours, and then holding them under good chill storage conditions.

10.7.8 Enterobacteriaceae

Enterobacteriaceae are a diverse group of bacteria that include both pathogenic organisms, such as *Salmonella, Yersinia* and *E. coli*, and with harmless organisms, many of which reside in the intestines of humans and other animals, including *Citrobacter* and *Enterobacter*. The group also includes a number of organisms that are associated with plant species, such as *Xanthamonas*. Enterobacteriaceae are very common in the general environment, in soil and on plant matter but, as they also readily colonise and grow outside the human/animal intestine, they can proliferate in the general factory environment. Enterobacteriaceae are used as indicators of process efficacy, cleaning efficacy and general hygienic conditions. They are frequently present in high numbers (10^2–10^3/g) in a variety of fresh salad and vegetables with little significance to product safety but, as they are readily destroyed by normal pasteurisation temperatures, their presence in low numbers (10–10^2/g) in cooked foods at the point of production is an indication of post-process contamination from poorly cleaned equipment or from poor handling practices. With some exceptions, Enterobacteriaceae do not tolerate low pH conditions (pH <4.5) and do not grow at low a_w (<0.95) and grow slowly, if at all, under good chill conditions <5 °C. In long-shelf-life products, Enterobacteriaceae can increase to high numbers at temperatures between 5 and 8 °C and occasionally cause product spoilage due to gas production (blowing of packs) or by the production of off-odours such as hydrogen sulfide. High levels at the beginning of life (>10^3/g) may be indicative of extensive post-process contamination or, indeed, inadequate processing of the material. Whilst they do not indicate a direct hazard to product safety, their unusual presence at high levels should be investigated to determine the significance in relation to process efficacy of cleaning/hygiene practices.

10.7.9 Yeasts and moulds

Yeasts and moulds are two distinct groups of fungi that cause significant amounts of product spoilage. They both occur in the general environment but are particularly associated with vegetation and are also used in the manufacture of fermented products, where they may occur as part of the natural flora, as in the case of mould-ripened cheeses or salamis. Both yeasts and moulds are generally destroyed by normal pasteurisation temperatures, but some fungi can produce heat-resistant spores capable of surviving at high temperature (80–90 °C). Both are capable of growth at low pH (<3.0) and low a_w (<0.7), although the moulds in general can grow at somewhat lower levels (*ca* 0.61). Strains of both organisms can grow at chill temperatures, although both grow fastest at warm ambient temperature (20–30 °C). The mechanism of spoilage does differ; moulds spoil foods by the production of a visible fungal colony that leads to rejection of the food due to overt visible spoilage. Yeasts, however, usually spoil foods as a result of their fermentation behaviour, producing gas (CO_2) from fermentable sugars, which causes 'blowing' of the product, and they may also produce large amounts of ethanol, causing flavour taints. Moulds can be inhibited in foods by the exclusion of oxygen, whereas yeasts can grow both aerobically and anaerobically. Control of both of these organisms is effected by thermal destruction and the operation of hygiene in the factory environment, particularly avoiding aerosols post-processing. To achieve stability, many foods, where permitted, employ effective preservatives such as sorbate or benzoate (200–1,000 ppm) to prevent growth of these organisms, but act best at low pH (<5.5). Levels of yeasts above 10^4/g or ml in products containing fermentable carbohydrates such as sucrose or fructose are likely to spoil rapidly without the use of preservatives.

10.7.10 *Pseudomonads*

Pseudomonads are a major cause of food spoilage in chilled perishable products, including ready meals. They are a group of bacteria that occur naturally in water, soil, vegetation and the general environment. Some strains can be pathogenic to humans, but this is not associated with foodborne transmission. *Pseudomonas* species capable of spoilage grow well at chill temperatures and selectively outgrow many other microorganisms that may also be present. They grow best under aerobic conditions and are readily destroyed by pasteurisation temperatures, frequently occurring in foods as post-process contaminants, principally from the production line and equipment. They do not tolerate low pH (<5.5) and do not grow well at low a_w (<0.96) and are therefore well suited to growth in near neutral pH, high water activity ready meals. They are frequently found in high numbers on raw meats, poultry and dairy products, where they also cause significant spoilage. Spoilage occurs through production of large amounts of enzymes, including proteases and lipases, which degrade constituents of the products, giving rise to flavour defects including putrid and rancid odours. Growth to high levels may also be accompanied by visual spoilage due to colony formation. Excluding oxygen in products by modified-atmosphere packing or vacuum packing can significantly reduce the growth of pseudomonads and therefore reduce spoilage.

10.7.11 *TVC (total viable count) / APC (aerobic plate count)*

Total viable count is the term commonly applied for the test to enumerate microorganisms in food using non-selective agar at a specified temperature (22–30 °C) under aerobic conditions. Whilst such a test is not strictly a count of total bacteria, as many bacteria present in the food may not grow at these temperatures or under these conditions, it does give a general indication of the bacterial population in the food and can be linked to the potential durability of the product. TVC is more properly referred to as an aerobic plate count (APC). The APC will usually detect lactic acid bacteria, yeasts, pseudomonads and Enterobacteriaceae and a wide selection of other bacteria, many of which are capable of product spoilage. Most often used for trend analysis purposes, high APC levels in a food at point of production may be an indication of poor standards of processing or inadequate plant or production hygiene.

It should be remembered that most fermented products will have naturally high aerobic plate counts due to the presence of starter culture bacteria, and such tests are usually not appropriate for these products.

References

1. Bell C., Kyriakides A. *Listeria: A Practical Approach to the Organism and its Control in Foods.* Oxford, Blackwell Science. 1998.
2. Bell C., Kyriakides A. *E. coli: A Practical Approach to the Organism and its Control in Foods.* Oxford, Blackwell Science. 1998.
3. Bell C., Kyriakides A. *Clostridium botulinum: A Practical Approach to the Organism and its Control in Foods.* Oxford, Blackwell Science. 2000.
4. Anon. *Safer Cooked Meat Production Guidelines. A 10-point Plan.* London, Department of Health. 1992.
5. Advisory Committee on the Microbiological Safety of Food. *Report on Vacuum Packaging and Associated Processes.* London, HMSO. 1992 and Annual Report 1995 Annex III.
6. van Netten P., Van de Moosdijk A., Van Hoensel P. *et al. Psychrotrophic strains of Bacillus cereus producing enterotoxin.* Journal of Applied Bacteriology, 1990, 69 (1), 73-9.
7. Labbe R. *Clostridium perfringens, in Foodborne Bacterial Pathogens;* edited by Doyle M.P., New York, Marcel Dekker Inc., 191-234. 1989.
8. Food and Drug Administration. *Potentially Hazardous Food, Hot and Cold Holding.* Food Code, Chapter 3: Food, Section 3-501.16, Washington, DC. 1999.
9. *Food MicroModel, Version 3.02,* Food MicroModel Ltd, Randalls Road, Leatherhead, Surrey, UK. 1999.
10. Chilled Foods Association. *Guidelines for Good Hygienic Practice in the Manufacture of Chilled Foods. (Third Edition).* London, CFA. 1997.
11. Anon. *A Code of Practice for Microbiology Laboratories Handling Food Samples. Guideline No. 9.* Gloucestershire, Campden and Chorleywood Food Research Association. 1996.
12. Institute of Food Science and Technology. *Development and Use of Microbiological Criteria for Foods.* London, IFST. 1999.
13. Gilbert R.J., de Louvois J., Donovan T. *et al. Guidelines for the microbiological quality of some ready-to-eat foods sampled at point of sale.* Communicable Disease and Public Health, 2000, 3 (3), 163-67.

INDEX